Mastering Arabic 1

Activity Book

Practice for beginners

Jane Wightwick &
Mahmoud Gaafar

HIPPOCRENE BOOKS, INC.
New York

Hippocrene Books, Inc. edition, 2011

First published by Palgrave Macmillan.

Published in North America under license from Macmillan Publishers Ltd,
Houndmills, Basingstoke, Hants RG21 6XS, United Kingdom.

ISBN 13: 978-0-7818-1269-6

ISBN 10: 0-7818-1269-0

Cataloging-in-Publication data available from the Library of Congress.

For more information, contact:
HIPPOCRENE BOOKS, INC.
171 Madison Avenue
New York, NY 10016
www.hippocrenebooks.com

Printed in China

Contents

Introduction

Practice, practice, practice!

The early stages of learning a new language are a steep learning curve, especially when you are also coping with an unfamiliar script as you are with Arabic. You really cannot have too much practice if you want the language to stick in the long term.

Mastering Arabic 1 Activity Book has been specifically developed to provide lively and enjoyable additional practice for beginners learning Arabic by themselves or within a group. The carefully graded activities will reinforce vocabulary and basic concepts in a variety of ways and so increase confidence and understanding of basic Arabic.

Mastering Arabic 1 Activity Book is especially suitable for use alongside the leading Arabic language course, *Mastering Arabic 1*, with the 20 units mirroring the main programme. The vocabulary and structures used in *Mastering Arabic 1 Activity Book* are also taken directly from the main course and reworked to provide additional reinforcement. However, *Mastering Arabic 1 Activity Book* is also very useful for others studying Arabic at a beginner level, and does not rely on a knowledge of the main course.

The *Mastering Arabic* series teaches the universally understood Modern Standard Arabic. However, as in the main course, whenever there are dialogues or situations where the colloquial language would naturally be used, we have tried to choose vocabulary and structures that are as close to the spoken form as possible. In this way, you will find that you are able to understand Arabic in a variety of different situations.

How to use *Mastering Arabic 1 Activity Book*

You can use *Mastering Arabic 1 Activity Book* to reinforce your learning as you go along. The contents section on pages 3 and 4 lists the main areas covered by the activities in each unit. Choose an activity that practises what you are currently learning.

Alternatively, you can use *Mastering Arabic 1 Activity Book* as a review of the basics of the Arabic language before moving on to a higher level. The answers at the back of the book will help you to assess your progress. Try to revisit areas where you feel uncertain. Then come back and try the activities again.

Acknowledgements

We would like to thank the following who reviewed the activities in this book: Taoufiq Cherkaoui, Petros Samano and Najiba Keane. The encouragement and valuable comments provided by these experienced Arabic teachers have made an important contribution to the book. We are also very grateful for the continuing support of the team at Palgrave Macmillan, particularly Helen Bugler, Isobel Munday and Phillipa Davidson-Blake.

unit 1

Getting started

1 Match the Arabic script to the pronunciation, as in the example.

[3] bu	[ ] tu
[ ] tha	[ ] thi
[ ] yu	[ ] ni
[ ] ya	[ ] ti
[ ] ba	[ ] na

1 بَ	6 يُ
2 تِ	7 ثَ
3 بُ	8 نِ
4 ثِ	9 تُ
5 نَ	10 يَ

Tip: Accustom yourself from the start to reading Arabic lists from top right to bottom left.

2 Write the vowel signs on these letters to match the pronunciation, as in the example.

1 nu نُ	**5** yi ي
2 ta ت	**6** tha ث
3 bi ب	**7** bu ب
4 thu ث	**8** tu ت

3 Complete the chart showing how the letters look at the beginning, in the middle and at the end of a word.

at the end	*in the middle*	*at the beginning*	*letter*
________	________	بـ	(bā’) ب
________	ـتـ	________	(tā’) ت
ـث	________	________	(thā’) ث
________	________	نـ	(nūn) ن
ـي	________	________	(yā’) ي

4 How many of the Arabic letters above can you find in this news headline? Circle the letters as in the example, and then note how many times each letter appears below.

ثابت البنّا وزير التعليم اللبناني
في البيت الأبيض يوم الثلاثاء

ب ☐   ت ☐   ث ☐   ن ☐   ي ☐

5 Handwriting practice

بنت bint (girl/daughter)

بيت bayt (house)

بنّ bunn (coffee beans)

بين bayna (between)

تبن tibn (hay)

Tip: Add the dots on the letter shapes *after* completing the main shape of the word.

6 Choose the correct alternative for joining these letters, as in the example.

1 ن + ت + ب = a نيب (b) نتب c تبن

2 ب + ن + ي = a بني b بين c نبي

3 ي + ث + ب = a يتب b يثب c ثيب

4 ت + ن + ن = a نتن b تبّ c تنّ

5 ي + ن + ب + ت = a يبت b يبنت c ينبت

6 ت + ث + ب + ت = a يثبت b نثبت c تثبت

7 ب + ي + ي + ن = a بيّن b بينّ c بّين

8 ن + ب + ن + ي = a بنبي b نبني c بنّي

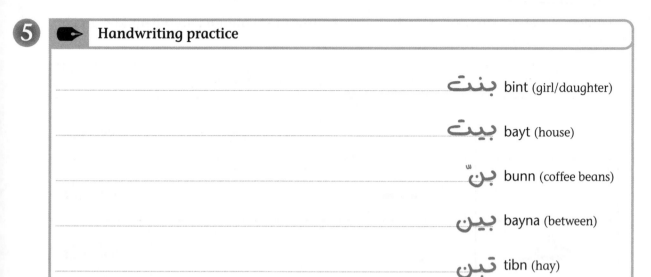

7 Arrange the letters and add the vowels to label the pictures, as in the example.

ت ب ي

1 بَيت

ن ب ت

2 ______

ن ب ي

3 ______

نّ ب

4 ______

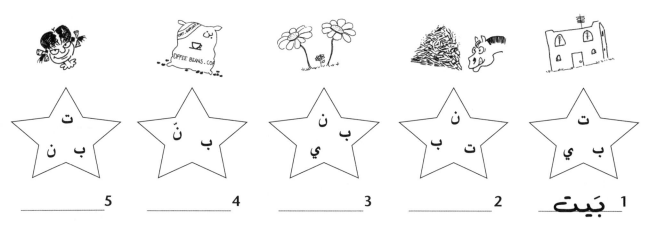

ت ب ن

5 ______

8

Conversation

Practise replying to these greetings. Try saying your reply out loud.

You may not be familiar yet with all the Arabic letters, so use the transliteration that follows to help you pronounce the words and write your response.

1 *(good morning)* صباح الخير ṣabāḥ al-khayr

______ *(reply)*

2 *(good evening)* مساء الخير masā' al-khayr

______ *(reply)*

3 *(hello)* أهلاً ahlan

______ *(reply to a male)*

4 *(hello)* أهلاً ahlan

______ *(reply to a female)*

unit 2

Putting words together

1 Eleven Arabic letters are hidden in this picture. Can you find them all?

2 Write the names by joining the letters, as in the example.
(Take care to leave a small space after the six non-joining letters.)

1 ن + و + ر = نور

2 ز + ي + ن = ____________

3 أ + ن + د + ي = ____________

4 ب + ا + ر + ي = ____________

5 ز + ي + د = ____________

6 أ + ن + و + ر = ____________

7 د + ا + ن + ي = ____________

8 ن + ا + د + ر = ____________

9 د + ي + ن + ا = ____________

10 ث + ا + ب + ت = ____________

3 Now join the two names together using و wa- ('and'), as in the example.

1 (Dina/Nour) دينا وَنور

2 (Andy/Zayn) ____________

3 (Anwar/Zayd) ____________

4 (Thabit/Barry) ____________

5 (Nour/Danny) ____________

6 (Barry/Nadir) ____________

7 (Anwar/Dina) ____________

8 (Nadir/Andy) ____________

4 **Handwriting practice**

أنا anā (I)

أنتَ anta (you, *masc.*)

أنتِ anti (you, *fem.*)

و wa- (and)

وأنت؟ wa-anta(-i) (and you?)

5 Choose the correct translation to match the speech bubble.

1 أنا زيد.
a I'm Zayn.
b I'm Zayd.
c You're Zayd.

2 أنا زين وأنت؟
a I'm Zayn, and you?
b I'm Zaynab, and you?
c Are you Zayn?

3 أنا أنور.
a I'm Nur.
b I'm Anwar.
c I'm Adnan.

4 أنتَ دينو؟
a Are you Dina?
b Are you Danny?
c Are you Dino?

5 أنت روزا.
a You're Rosa.
b You're Rose.
c I'm Rose.

6 أنا بدر وأنت؟
a I'm Brad, and you?
b I'm Bart, and you?
c I'm Badr, and you?

6 How do you say these in Arabic?

1 I'm Zayd. أنا زيد.

2 I'm Nour, and you *(fem.)*? __________

3 I'm Badr, and you *(masc.)*? __________

4 I'm Danny. __________

5 Are you Anwar? __________

6 Are you Zaynab? __________

7 **Conversation**

You have just bumped into a friend, Zaynab. She is with her brother, Anwar, whom you haven't met before. Prepare your half of the conversation and try saying it out loud. As before, you can use the transliteration that follows the Arabic script to help you pronounce the words and write your response until you are familiar with all the Arabic letters.

Use the English prompts to guide you, as in the example.

أنت: *Hello, Zaynab.* أهلاً يا زينب. ahlan yā zaynab.

زينب: أهلاً بك. ahlan bik(i).

أنت: *How are you?* __________

زينب: الحمد لله. al-ḥamdu lillāh.

أنت: *Are you Anwar?* __________

أنور: نعم، أنا أنور. naعam *(yes)*, anā anwar.

أنت: *Pleased to meet you, Anwar.* __________

أنور: تشرّفنا. tasharrafnā.

unit 3

The family

1 Match the letter combinations to their joined-up equivalents.

1	م + ه + ا	a	حامد
2	ح + ا + م + د	b	ماري
3	ه + ا + ن + ي	c	حاتم
4	ح + ا + ت + م	d	مها
5	م + ا + ر + ي	e	ياسمين
6	ي + ا + س + م + ي + ن	f	هاني

2 **Handwriting practice**

هذا hādha (this, *masc.*)

هذه hādhihi (this, *fem.*)

زجاجة zujāja (bottle)

خيمة khayma (tent)

أحمد aḥmad (Ahmed)

هو huwa (he)

هي hiya (she)

Tip: The letter hā' (ه) needs special attention. The letter shape varies considerably depending on its position, and hā' also has an alternative shape in the middle (ـهـ or ـهـ).

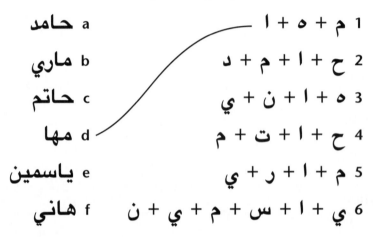

3 Look at the picture and find the word in the word square. (The words can be found running right to left or top to bottom.) Then write the Arabic joined up next to the picture and decide if the word is masculine (M) or feminine (F), as in the example.

ث	ا	ذ	د	ت	ي	ب
ة	ر	خ	م	ر	ه	ن
ج	ب	ي	ت	ي	ذ	ت
ر	ا	م	ح	ذ	ث	ر
ي	ث	ة	ج	ا	ج	د
د	ا	م	ح	ب	م	ه
ة	ج	ا	ج	ز	ي	ذ

1  زُجاجة F

2  ______ ☐

3  ______ ☐

4  ______ ☐

5  ______ ☐

6  ______ ☐

7  ______ ☐

8  ______ ☐

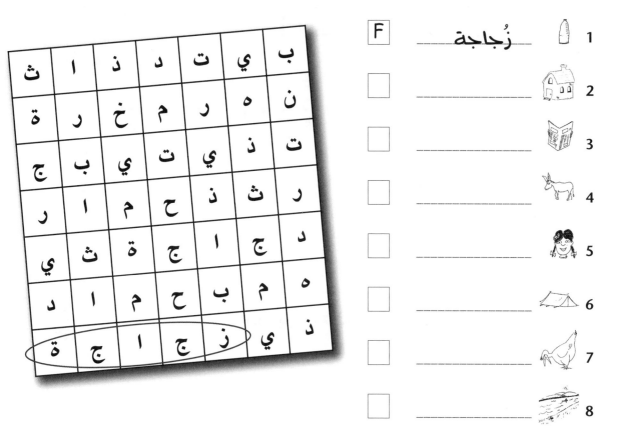

4 Re-write the words below, adding the ending ي -ī ('my'), as in the example.

1 أَخ (brother) ⟵ أخي (my brother)

2 أَب (father) ⟵ ______

3 أُمّ (mother) ⟵ ______

4 أُخت (sister) ⟵ ______

5 إِبن (son) ⟵ ______

6 بِنت (daughter) ⟵ ______

7 زَوج (husband) ⟵ ______

8 زَوجة (wife) ⟵ ______

9 بَيت (house) ⟵ ______

10 مَدينة (city/town) ⟵ ______

Tip: When you add the ending, adjust the final letter to the joining shape and remember that the feminine ending tā' marbūṭa (ة) is then written and pronounced as a regular tā' (تـ).

5 Complete the names of the family members on the family trees below, according to what the people are saying.

أنا حامِد وأنا زوج نادِية.
أنا مَها، أُم داني وماري.
أنا بدر، اِبن حامد ونادِية.
أنا ماري وهذا أخي داني.
أنا زيزي، أُخت بَدر.
وأنا؟ أنا أيمَن... زَوج مها.

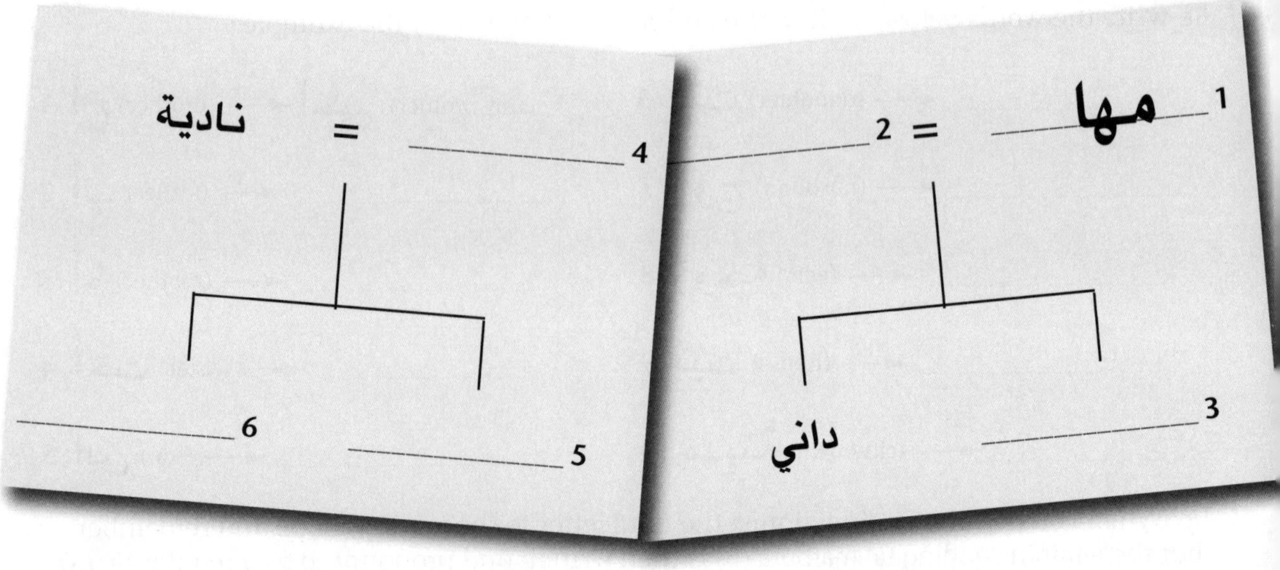
نادية = ____ 4
6 ____
5 ____
1 ____ مها = ____ 2
داني
3 ____

6 How do you say these in Arabic?

1 This is my husband, Hamed. هذا زوجي، حامد.

2 This is my mother, Maha. ____________

3 Mary is Ayman's daughter. ____________

4 Nadia is Hamed's wife. ____________

5 Who's Badr? He's my son. ____________

6 Who's Mary? She's my daughter. ____________

7 **Conversation**

Your father and your little sister are seeing you off at the train station when you bump into your friend Zaynab again. (Note: train = قطار qiṭār)

Prepare your half of the conversation introducing your father and sister to Zaynab and try saying it out loud. Remember that you can use the transliteration to help you pronounce the words and write your response; but you may also now want to have a go at writing some of the words in Arabic script.

Use the English prompts to guide you, as in the example.

زينب: أهلاً. ahlan.

أنت: *How are you, Zaynab?* كيف الحال يا زينب؟ kayf al-ḥāl yā zaynab?

زينب: الحمد الله al-ḥamdu lillāh.

أنت: *Zaynab, this is my father.* ____________

زينب: تشرّفنا. ومن هذه؟ tasharrafnā. wa-man hādhihi?

أنت: *This is Mimi. She's my sister.* ____________

زينب: أهلاً يا ميمي! ahlan yā mīmī!

أنت: *Ah, this is my train.* ____________

زينب: مع السلامة! maɛa s-salāma!

أنت: *Goodbye!* ____________

unit 4

Jobs

1 Complete the chart showing how these letters look at the beginning, in the middle and at the end of a word.

at the end	*in the middle*	*at the beginning*	*letter*
		ســ	(sīn) س
	ـشـ		(shīn) ش
		صـ	(ṣād) ص
ـض			(ḍād) ض

2 **Handwriting practice**

باص bāṣ (bus)

شورت shūrt (shorts)

سينما sīnimā (cinema)

مدرّس mudarris (teacher)

محاسب muḥāsib (accountant)

ممرّضة mumariḍḍa (nurse)

3 Match the members of the football team with their Arabic names, as in the example.

زيدان	7	أمين	☐
ميدو	☐	منير	☐
حبيب	☐	خيري	☐
شحاتة	☐	حمدي	☐
نصري	☐	أبو زيد	☐
حسن	☐		

4 Read what Sara tells you about her family in the picture and complete the table below.

أنا سارة وأنا مُدرّسة. هذا زوجي، حَسَن. هو مُراسل.

هذه بنتي، ياسمين، وهي مُحاسبة. وابني، أمين مُهندس.

وهذه هي أُمّي سميرة بَينَ ياسمين وأمين. أُمّي ممرّضة.

name	relationship to Sara	job
Sara	—	teacher

5 Make the sentences plural, as in the example.

(They're carpenters.) هم نجّارون .	1 هو نجّار.
	2 هو خبّاز.
	3 أنا مهندس.
	4 هي مدرّسة.
	5 أنا محاسبة.
	6 هو مدرّس.
	7 هي مهندسة.
	8 هي ممرّضة.

6 **Conversation**

You are talking to Sara about jobs, and what your families do for a living.
Prepare your half of the conversation and try saying it out loud.
Use the English prompts to guide you, as in the example.

أنت:	mā ʿamalik yā sāra? ما عملِك يا سارة؟ *What's your job, Sara?*
سارة:	anā mudarrisa. w-anta(-i)? أنا مدرّسة. وأنت؟
أنت:	*I'm a student. My father is a baker.*
سارة:	āh! anā akhī khabbāz! آه! أنا أخي خبّاز!
أنت:	*What's your husband's job?*
سارة:	huwa murāsil. هو مراسل.
أنت:	*And your son and your daughter?*
سارة:	amīn muhandis wa-yāsmīn muḥāsiba. أمين مهندس وياسمين محاسبة.
أنت:	*Wonderful!*

unit 5

Describing things

1 Match the letter combinations to their joined-up equivalents.

a قام	1 م + ل + ف
b كاف	2 ق + ا + م
c ملف	3 ك + ف + ل
d قلم	4 ق + ل + م
e كفل	5 ف + ل + ك
f فلك	6 ك + ا + ف

2 **Handwriting practice**

كلب kalb (dog)

قلم qalam (pen)

مكسور maksūr (broken)

خفيف khafīf (light)

ممكن؟ mumkin? (may I?)

تفضّل tafaḍḍal (here you are)

شكراً shukran (thank you)

Tip: You may find it helps the flow of your writing to add any dots on the letter shapes and the top stroke of the kaaf (كـ) *after* completing the main shape of the word.

3 Arrange the letters and add the vowels to label the pictures, as in the example:

1 قَلَم ______

2 ______

3 ______

4 ______

5 ______

6 ______

7 ______

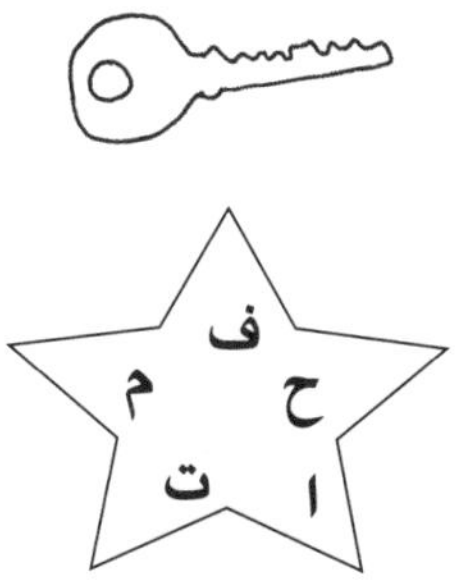

8 ______

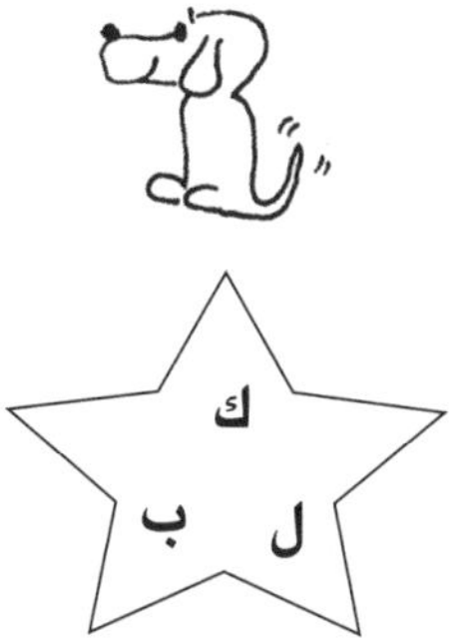

9 ______

10 ______

4 هذا or هذه?
Write the words from Activity 3 in the correct column, as in the example.

هذه...	هذا...
	هذا قلم.

5 True or false? Look at the picture of Warda and decide which sentences are true.

1 زجاجة وردة مكسورة. ✔

2 درّاجة وردة جديدة.

3 شورت وردة أسود...

4 ...وقميصها أبيض.

5 خيمة وردة سليمة.

6 كتاب وردة ثقيل...

7 ...وهو كتاب قديم.

8 خاتم وردة جميل.

6 Change 'a' to 'the' by adding الـ... (al-), as in the example .

1 بيت (a house) ⟵ البيت (the house)

2 ولد (a boy) ⟵ ______________

3 نهر (a river) ⟵ ______________

4 زجاجة (a bottle) ⟵ ______________

5 مفتاح (a key) ⟵ ______________

6 جريدة (a newspaper) ⟵ ______________

7 تلميذ (a pupil) ⟵ ______________

8 قلم (a pen) ⟵ ______________

9 مدينة (a city) ⟵ ______________

10 خبّاز (a baker) ⟵ ______________

7

Conversation

You are in an Arabic-speaking country and need to write a quick shopping list.
You don't have a pen but you've noticed some for sale on a nearby newspaper stand.
Prepare your half of the conversation with the seller (البائع al-bā'iع) and try saying it out loud.
Use the English prompts to guide you, as in the example.

أنت: *Good morning* صباح الخير . ṣabāḥ al-khayr. ______________

البائع: صباح النور. ṣabāḥ an-nūr

أنت: *May I have (*ممكن *mumkin) a pen, please?* ______________

البائع: هذا القلم؟ hādhā l-qalam?

أنت: *No. I'd like the black [one].* ______________

البائع: تَفَضَّل(ي). tafaḍḍal(ī).

أنت: *This pen is broken!* ______________

البائع: تَفَضَّل(ي). هذا القلم سليم. tafaḍḍal(ī). hādhā l-qalam salīm.

أنت: *Thank you.* ______________

البائع: مع السلامة. maعa s-salāma.

أنت: *Goodbye.* ______________

unit 6

Where is it?

1 Complete the chart showing how the letters look at the beginning, in the middle and at the end of a word.

at the end	*in the middle*	*at the beginning*	*letter*
		طـ	ط (ṭā')
ـظ			ظ (ẓā')
	ـعـ		ع (ʿayn)
		غـ	غ (ghayn)

Tip: The letters ʿayn (ع) and ghayn (غ) change their shape significantly when they join.

2 Choose one of the letters in the table above to complete the word according to the English in brackets, as in the example.

1 عـرب (Arabs)

2 ☐ـالب (student)

3 ☐ـمل (work)

4 ☐ـزّة (Gaza)

5 مالـ☐ـة (Malta)

6 بـ☐ـداد (Baghdad)

6 قـ☐ـر (Qatar)

8 أبو ☐ـبي (Abu Dhabi)

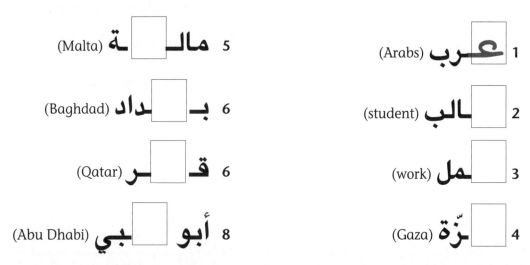

3 Match the pictures to the correct positional word.

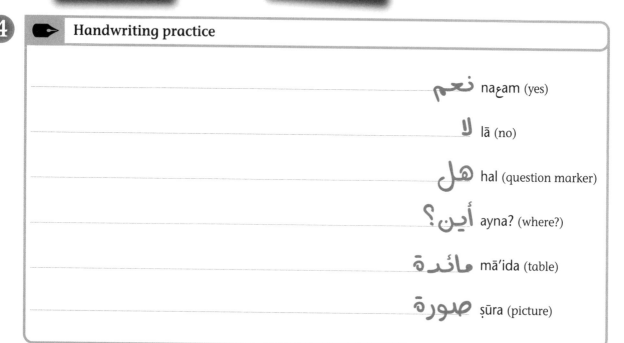

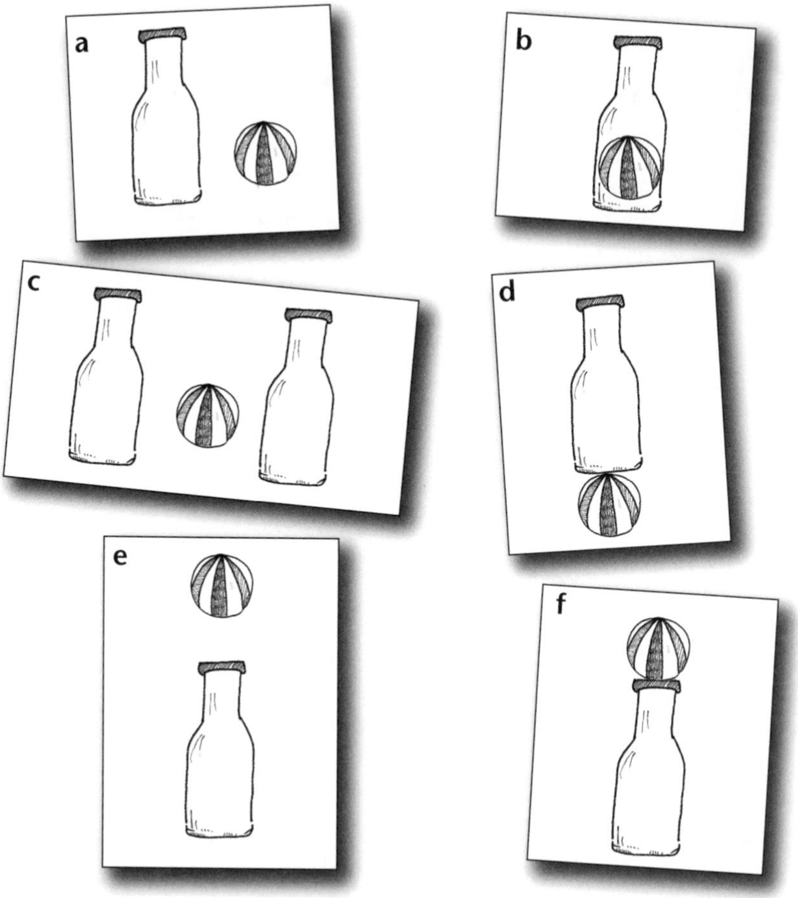

1 فوق

2 على

3 بجانب

4 بين

5 في

6 تحت

4 **Handwriting practice**

نعم naعam (yes)

لا lā (no)

هل hal (question marker)

أين؟ ayna? (where?)

مائدة mā'ida (table)

صورة ṣūra (picture)

5 Make sentences or questions from the picture prompts, as in the example.

1  تحت . الخاتم تحت الكرسيّ.

2  في . ____________

3 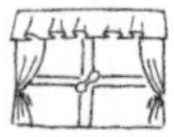 فوق 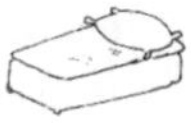. ____________

4  في ؟ ____________

5  على ؟ ____________

6  بجانب . ____________

7 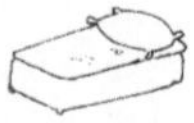 بين 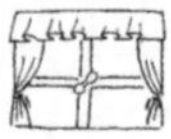 و . ____________

8  بين  و ؟ ____________

6 In Arabic, try to describe the position of some items you see in the room you are currently using, or one you can easily visualise. Use your sentences above as models.

7 Write questions using the prompts, as in the example .

1 سَرير (bed) ⟵ هل هذا سرير؟ ____________

2 شبّاك (window) ⟵ ____________

3 صورة (picture) ⟵ ____________

4 باب (door) ⟵ ____________

5 تليفزيون (television) ⟵ ____________

6 خزانة (cupboard) ⟵ ____________

7 كرسيّ (chair) ⟵ ____________

8 مائدة (table) ⟵ ____________

8 **Conversation**

You have found an interesting restaurant, and are asking the maitre d' (المتر) about a table. Prepare your half of the conversation and try saying it out loud. You should be able to have a go at writing your part. Use the English prompts to guide you, as in the example.

أنت: *Good evening.* مساء الخير. masā' al-khayr. ____________

المتر : مساء النور. masā' an-nūr.

أنت: *I'd like a table.* ____________

المتر : نعم. naعam.

أنت: *A table beside the window, please.* ____________

المتر : هذه المائدة؟ hādhihi l-mā'ida?

أنت: *Yes, the table under the picture.* ____________

المتر : تَفَضَّل(ي). tafaḍḍal(ī).

أنت: *Lovely ['beautiful']. Thank you!* ____________

unit 7

Describing places

1 Handwriting practice

مدينة madīna (town)

غرفة ghurfa (room)

بنك bank (bank)

مدرسة madrasa (school)

مصنع maṣnaع (factory)

شارع shāriع (street)

مستشفى mustashfā (hospital)

2 How do you say these in Arabic?

1 a small factory مصنع صغير

2 the small factory

3 a big town

4 the big town

5 my new shirt

6 his big black dog

7 He's strong.

8 She's a tall girl.

3 Yusuf is on a student exchange and has written an email to his mother. Read the email and answer the questions in English.

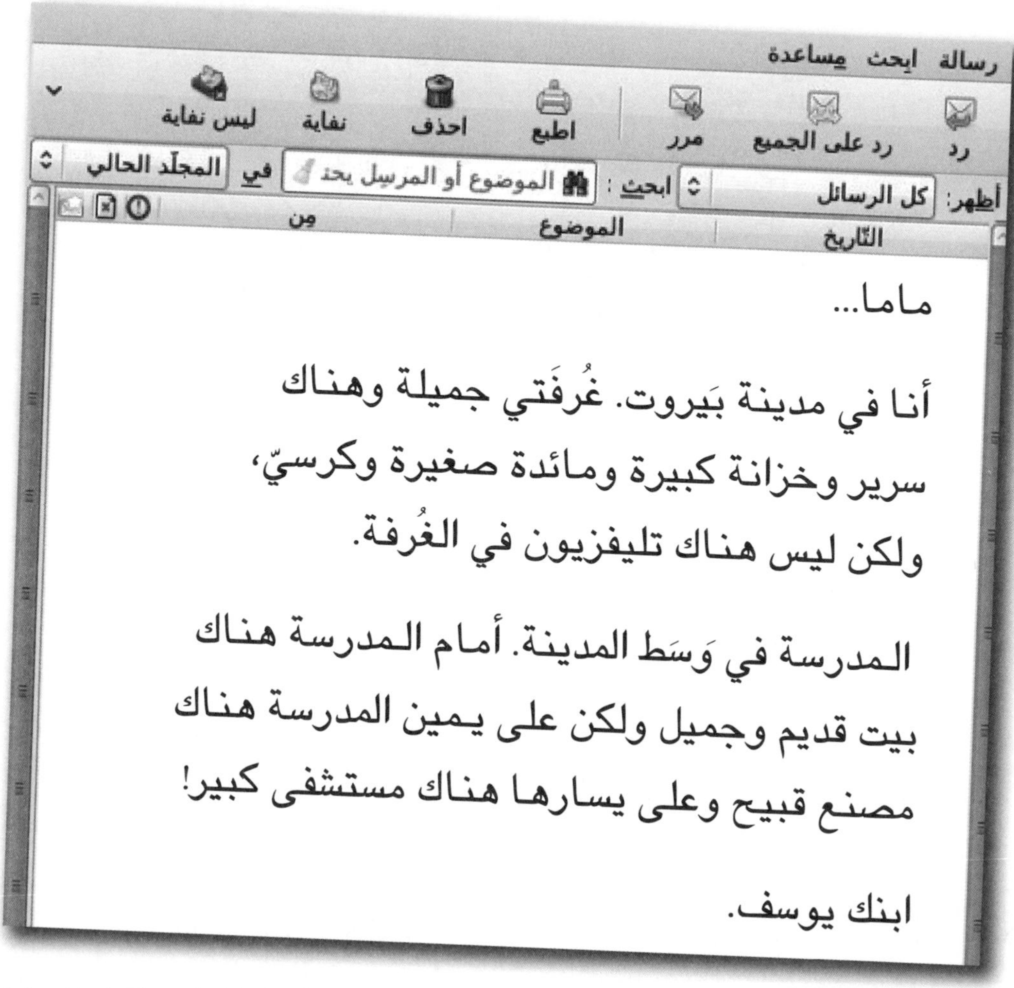

ماما...

أنا في مدينة بَيروت. غُرفَتي جميلة وهناك سرير وخزانة كبيرة ومائدة صغيرة وكرسيّ، ولكن ليس هناك تليفزيون في الغُرفة.

المدرسة في وَسَط المدينة. أمام المدرسة هناك بيت قديم وجميل ولكن على يمين المدرسة هناك مصنع قبيح وعلى يسارها هناك مستشفى كبير!

ابنك يوسف.

1 Which city is Yusuf visiting?

2 Does he like his room?

3 Is the cupboard big or small?

4 Is there a table and chair in the room?

5 Is there a television?

6 Where is the school?

7 What is there in front of the school?

8 What two other buildings does Yusuf mention?

9 Why does Yusuf put an exclamation mark at the end of his email?

10 How does he sign off?

4 Mark the correct column depending on whether you can see the item in the picture or not, as in the example.

	هناك...	ليس هناك...
1 سيّارة		✗
2 باص		
3 بنت		
4 ولد		
5 كتاب		
6 قلم		
7 باب		
8 كلب		
9 مائدة		

	هناك...	ليس هناك...
10 كرسيّ		
11 حمامة		
12 تينة		
13 دجاجة		
14 زجاجة		
15 شجرة		
16 درّاجة		
17 وردة		
18 ذبابة		

5 Now complete this description of the picture on page 32. (Note: أو aw = or)

في هذه الصورة هناك شجرة كبيرة. ________ الشجرة هناك

________ ثقيلة وكرسيّ. بجانب الكرسيّ هناك ________ صغيرة.

في وسط الصورة هناك ________ وهو على ________ .

________ الولد هناك بنت. كلب البنت أسود و________ .

________ المائدة هناك زجاجة كولا ووردة ولكن ________

هناك قلم أو ________ .

6 **Conversation**

You are in a small Arabic-speaking town and you need to withdraw some money. You're not sure if there is a bank so you stop a man (رَجُل rajul) on the street to ask.

Prepare your half of the conversation and try saying it out loud as usual.

Use the English prompts to guide you, as in the example.

أنت:	*Good morning.*	صباح الخير. ṣabāḥ al-khayr.
الرجل:		صباح النور. ṣabāḥ an-nūr
أنت:	*Is there a bank in the town?*	________
الرجل:		نعم. بجانب المدرسة. naعam. bijānib al-madrasa.
أنت:	*On the right of the school?*	________
الرجل:		لا، على يسارها. lā, عalā yasār-hā.
أنت:	*Thank you. Goodbye.*	________
الرجل:		مع السلامة. maعa s-salāma.

unit 8

Review

1 Complete the Arabic alphabet table and note whether the letter is a sun or a moon letter.

sun/moon letter	Arabic script	name of letter
		ḍād
		ṭā’
		ẓā’
		ɛayn
		ghayn
		fā’
		qāf
		kāf
		lām
		mīm
		nūn
		hā’
		wāw
		yā’

sun/moon letter	Arabic script	name of letter
moon	ا	alif
		bā’
		tā’
		thā’
		jīm
		ḥā’
		khā’
		dāl
		dhāl
		rā’
		zāy
		sīn
		shīn
		ṣād

Tip: Sun letters assimilate (take over) the ‘l’ sound when ‘al-’ (the) is added. Sun letters tend to be pronounced at the front of the mouth/with the teeth, while moon letters are those sounded further back in the mouth and do not affect the pronunciation of ‘al-’.

2 Look at the picture clues and complete the crossword. Remember that Arabic crosswords are compiled using the separate form of the letters. One clue is completed for you.

أُفقيّ ←

رَأسيّ ↓

3 Re-write the words below, using the appropriate possessive ending, as in the example.

1 بيت (her) ← بيتها (her house)

2 أب (my) ← ____________

3 كتاب (his) ← ____________

4 غُرفة (my) ← ____________

5 اِبن (your *masc.*) ← ____________

6 درّاجة (your *fem.*) ← ____________

7 زَوج (her) ← ____________

8 مَدرَسة (our) ← ____________

9 مَدينة (their *masc.*) ← ____________

10 سيّارة (their *masc.*) ← ____________

4 Read the description of Karim and his house and decide if the sentences are true or false.

كريم طالِب في المَدرَسة. أبو كريم مُهندِس
وأمّه مُمرّضة. بَيتهم في وَسط المدينة بِجانب
المدرسة. هناك شجَر جَميل أمام البيت.

البيت كبير ولكنّ غُرفة كريم صغيرة.
في غرفته هُناكَ سرير تحت الشبّاك
وخَزانة صَغيرة ومائدة. فوق المائدة
هناك تليفزيون ولكن ليس هناك كتاب!

	True	False
1 Karim is a school teacher.	❑	❑
2 His father is an accountant.	❑	❑
3 His mother is a nurse.	❑	❑
4 Their house is in the centre of town.	❑	❑
5 The house is small.	❑	❑
6 Karim's room is small.	❑	❑
7 There isn't a window in Karim's room.	❑	❑
8 There's a table in his room.	❑	❑
9 There's a television on the table.	❑	❑
10 Karim has lots of books.	❑	❑

5 How do you say these in Arabic?

1 The newspaper is under the chair. الجريدة تحت الكرسيّ.

2 There's a dog in the room. ______

3 There isn't a school in this town. ______

4 Is your *(masc.)* house big? ______

5 This is Zayn's bag. ______

6 Where's my mother? She's in the bank. ______

6 **Conversation**

You have made a reservation at a hotel and have now arrived at reception.

Prepare your half of the conversation with the hotel employee (المُوَظّف) and try saying it out loud. Remember you can use the transliteration that follows the Arabic to help you pronounce and write your answers, but you may now also want to have a go at writing some of it in Arabic script.

Use the English prompts to guide you, as in the example. (Note: internet = إنترنت)

الموظّف: الاسم من فضلك. al-ism min faḍlak?

أنت: *My name is Tom Lewis.* اسمي توم لويس. ismī Tom Lewis.

الموظّف: لويس... نعم. هذا هو المفتاح. Lewis..., naɛam. hādhā huwa l-miftāḥ.

أنت: *Thank you. Where's our room?* ______

الموظّف: فوق الكافيتريا. fawqa l-kāfītiryā.

أنت: *The bag is in the car. It's heavy.* ______

الموظّف: أحمد! الحقيبة من فضلك! aḥmad! al-ḥaqība min faḍlak!

أنت: *And is there internet in the room?* ______

الموظّف: نعم يا سيّد لويس. naɛam yā sayyid Lewis.

أنت: *Thank you.* ______

unit

9 Countries and people

1 Match the capital cities to the countries, as in the example.

بَغداد a	1 مِصر
عَمّان b	2 السودان
الرِّياض c	3 عُمان
القاهِرة d	4 ليبيا
الخَرطوم e	5 اليَمَن
دِمَشق f	6 العِراق
بَيروت g	7 سوريا
صَنعاء h	8 السَّعوديّة
مَسقَط i	9 لُبنان
طَرابلُس j	10 الأُردُنّ

2 Now describe the position of the cities using the prompts, as in the example.

1 عمّان/شمال ← عمّان في شمال الأردنّ. (Amman is in the north of Jordan.)

2 طرابلس/غَرب ← ______

3 نيو يورك/شَرق ← ______

4 لُندن/جَنوب ← ______

5 بيروت/غرب ← ______

6 your [nearest] city ← ______

3 Fill in the chart below with the personal information about these five people.

name	*nationality*	*home town*
Tom	English	Oxford

4 Describe the nationality of the people, as in the example.

1 جاك من باريس. (Jacques is from Paris) هو فرنسيّ. (He's French.) ______

2 حُسَين من بغداد. ______

3 نادية من دمشق. ______

4 هذا الولد من لُندُن. ______

5 هذه البنت من الخرطوم. ______

6 المهندسون من القاهرة. ______

7 المراسلون من روما. ______

8 المدرّسات من توكيو. ______

5 Complete the gaps in the paragraph about Jacques, using the words in the box. You can only use a word once. The first gap has been completed for you.

وسط مراسلة البنك أمّ لبنان ~~فرنسيّ~~ مستشفى من في جنوب

جاك فرنسيّ من باريس. أبو جاك ______ تولوز في ______ فرنسا ولكن أُمّه من بيروت في ______. جاك محاسب في ______ اللبنانيّ في ______ المدينة. أبو جاك مهندس ______ مصنع صغير وأُخته ______ لِجريدة لُبنانيّة في باريس. ______ جاك ممرّضة في ______ بجانب بَيتهم.

6 Try to describe where you and your family come from and what they do, using the paragraph in Activity 5 as a model. You can talk about yourself, your mother and father, your siblings, your partner or your children.

7

Conversation

You are talking to Sara about where you are from. Prepare your half of the conversation and try saying it out loud. Use the English prompts to guide you, as in the example.

When you've finished, you can try the conversation again, this time substituting your own details.

أنت: *Where are you from, Sara?* anti min ayna yā sāra? أنتِ من أين يا سارة؟

سارة: أنا عراقيّة من البصرة. وأنت؟ anā ɛirāqīyya min al-baṣra. w-anta(-i)?

أنت: *I'm English...*

...but my mother is American.

سارة: أنت من أيّة مدينة؟ anta(-i) min ayyat madīna?

أنت: *I'm from Leeds.*

سارة: أين هذه المدينة؟ ayna hādhihi l-madīna?

أنت: *It's in the north of England.*

سارة: هل ليدز صغيرة؟ hal Leeds ṣaghīra?

أنت: *No. It's a big town.*

unit 10 Counting things

1 Write the Arabic figure next to the number; then put them in order, from the lowest to the highest.

a سِتّة ☐ ٦
b ثَلاثة ☐
c واحِد ☐
d سَبعة ☐
e أربَعة ☐
f عَشَرة ☐
g اِثنان ☐
h تِسعة ☐
i ثَمانية ☐
j خَمسة ☐

2 بِكَم؟ How much? Decide how much money there is, as in the example.

١  أربعة جنيهات

٢  ______________

٣ 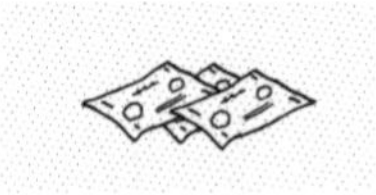 ______________

٤  ______________

٥  ______________

٦  ______________

٧  ______________

٨  ______________

3 Arrange the letters to label the pictures of things you can buy in the market, as in the example.

و ز م

١ موز

فّ ا ت ح

٢ ________

ن ل د ص

٣ ________

ق ب ط

٤ ________

ي ت ر ي ش ت

٥ ________

ط ا م م ط

٦ ________

ة ل ب ط

٧ ________

ن م ج ة

٨ ________

ة لّ س

٩ ________

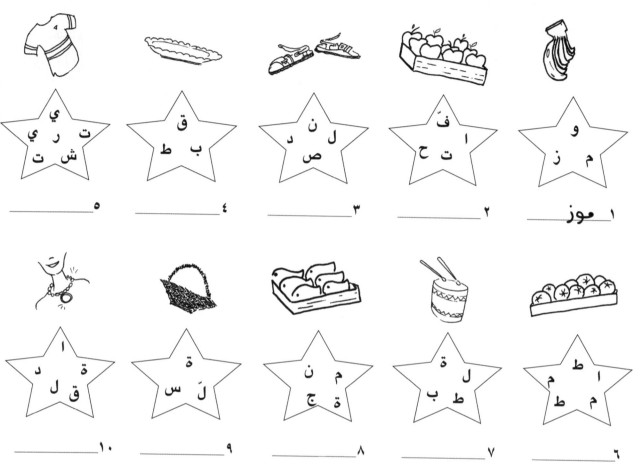

ا د ة ق ل

١٠ ________

4 Make the words refer to two of something using the dual ending, as in the example.

١ سوق ← سوقان (two markets)

٢ طَبَق ← ________

٣ سلّة ← ________

٤ كيس ← ________

٥ قَميص ← ________

٦ خاتم ← ________

٧ طَبلة ← ________

٨ حقيبة ← ________

٩ قَلَم ← ________

١٠ قِلادة ← ________

Tip: The dual ending has two alternatives: -ān (ان) and -ayn (يَن). Both endings are used in Modern Standard depending on the context, but -ayn is more common in spoken dialects.

5 Rewrite this conversation in the bazaar in the right order, as in the example.

جميل. بكم هذا، من فضلك؟

صندل جلد؟ الصندل الأبيَض جميل.

لا، أريد صندل جِلد من فضلك.

تفضّل. عشرة جنيهات.

نعم. عِندَنا هذا الصندل.

أهلاً. صباح الخير!

صباح النور. هل عِندَكُم صَندَل؟

شكراً، مع السلامة.

بعشرة جنيهات.

– أهلاً. صباح الخير!

6 How do you say these in Arabic?

١ How much is the drum? بكم الطبلة؟

٢ How much is a kilo of the apples?

٣ The necklace is ten pounds.

٤ The basket is seven pounds.

٥ A kilo of the tomotoes is three pounds.

٦ How much is the copper plate?

٧ The leather sandals are eight pounds.

7 **Conversation**

You are in the market and want to buy some fruit and vegetables from a stall.
Prepare your half of the conversation with the seller (البائع) and try saying it out loud.
Use the English prompts to guide you, as in the example.

أنت: *Do you have any oranges?* hal ꜥindakum burtuqāl? هل عندكم برتقال؟

البائع: عندنا إسبانيّ ومصريّ. ꜥindanā isbānīy wa-miṣrīy.

أنت: *A kilo of the Egyptian [ones], please.* ______

البائع: تفضّل(ي). tafaḍḍal(ī).

أنت: *And how much are the potatoes?* ______

البائع: الكيلو بجنيه. al-kīlū bi-junayh.

أنت: *Three kilos, please. How much is that?* ______

البائع: ٩ جنيهات، من فضلك. tisꜥa junayhāt, min faḍlak(-ik).

أنت: *Here you are. Do you have a bag?* ______

البائع: تفضّل(ي). مع السلامة. tafaḍḍal(ī). maꜥa s-salāma.

unit 11

Plurals and colours

1 Identify the root letters of the word on the right and then fill in its meaning and plural.

plural	*meaning*	*root letters*	*word*
أقلام	pen	ق/ل/م	قَلَم
			طَبَق
			قَلب
			مُدَرِّس
			صاحِب
			سيّارة
			سَيف
			وَلَد
			لَون
			حَفلة
			كوب
			شَمعة
			مُراسِل
			كيس
			مُمَرِّضة

2 Now describe what you own using the picture prompts, as in the example.

١  هذه هي أقلامي. (These are my pens.) ____________________

٢  ____________________

٣  ____________________

٣ 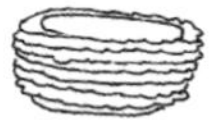 ____________________

٥  ____________________

٦ 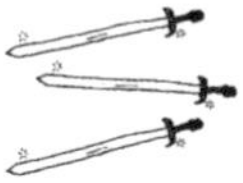 ____________________

٧  ____________________

٨  ____________________

٩  ____________________

١٠  ____________________

Tip: Only use the plural word هـؤلاء hā'ulā'i (these) and the pronouns هم hum/هنّ hunna (they) when referring to people in the plural. Remember that in Arabic the plural of objects is referred to in the *feminine singular*.

3 Use the key to colour the grid and reveal the picture.

٤	٤	٥	٤	٤	٤	٤	٤	٤	٤	٤
٤	٥	٥	٥	٥	٥	٥	٥	٥	٥	٤
٤	٦	٦	٦	٦	٦	٦	٦	٦	٦	٤
٤	٦	١	١	٦	٦	٦	١	١	٦	٤
٤	٦	١	١	٦	٦	٦	١	١	٦	٤
٤	٦	٦	٦	٦	٦	٦	٦	٦	٦	٤
٣	٦	٦	٦	٢	٢	٢	٦	٦	٦	٣
٣	٦	٦	٦	٢	٢	٢	٦	٦	٦	٣
٣	٦	٦	٦	٢	٢	٢	٦	٦	٦	٣

١ أبيض   ٤ أزرق
٢ أسود   ٥ أحمر
٣ أخضر   ٦ أصفر

ما هذا؟

هذا ________ .

4 Ahmed is going on on a trip to Paris and has made a list of all the things his family has asked him to bring back. Look at the list below and fill in the table on page 49 with the details of the items, as in the example.

بابا: قميص أبيض (قُطن) للحفلات
طارِق: حقيبة جلد سوداء للمدرسة
راندا: أقلام للكتابة (أحمر وأسود)
عادِل: خيمة زرقاء (خفيفة)
ماما: أفلام فرنسيّة قديمة
نونو: صندل بلاستيك صغير (أخضر)
ميمي: قبّعة صفراء (قطن أو حرير)

who?	*item(s)*	*description*
Dad	shirt	white (cotton) for parties

5 Conversation

You are in a clothes shop and want to buy a cotton T-shirt and hat. Prepare your half of the conversation with the seller and try saying it out loud. Use the English prompts to guide you as usual.

أنت: *I'd like a cotton T-shirt.* ______________________

البائع: حاضر. عندنا كلّ الألوان. ḥāḍir. ʿindanā kull il-alwān.

أنت: *I prefer the blue [one].* ______________________

البائع: تفضّل(ي). tafaḍḍal(ī).

أنت: *And do you have cotton hats?* ______________________

البائع: نعم... أيّ لون؟ naʿam... ayy lawn?

أنت: *The white hat.* ______________________

البائع: ٨ ريالات من فضلك. thamānyat riyālāt min faḍlak(-ik).

أنت: *Here you are. Thank you.* ______________________

unit 12 What happened yesterday?

1 Match the Arabic verbs to the English equivalent, as in the example.

I opened	**a**	١	شَرِبْتُ
I sat	**b**	٢	خَرَجْتُ
I heard	**c**	٣	كَتَبْتُ
I drank	**d**	٤	فَتَحْتُ
I found	**e**	٥	رَجَعْتُ
I went	**f**	٦	أَكَلْتُ
I returned	**g**	٧	جَلَسْتُ
I went out	**h**	٨	سَمِعْتُ
I ate	**i**	٩	ذَهَبْتُ
I wrote	**j**	١٠	وَجَدْتُ

2 Describe what you did yesterday using the picture prompts and one of the verbs in Activity 1, as in the example.

١  شرِبتُ فنجان شاي.

٢  ______________________

٣  ______________________

٤  ______________________

٥  ______________________

٦  ______________________

٧  ______________________

٨  ______________________

3 Write these verbs to refer to the correct person, as in the example.

١ ذهب (هي) ← ذَهَبَت (she went)

٢ شرب (أنا) ← ______________

٣ كتب (هو) ← ______________

٤ فتح (أنتَ) ← ______________

٥ أكل (أنتِ) ← ______________

٦ وجد (أنتَ) ← ______________

٧ خرج (هو) ← ______________

٨ جلس (أنتِ) ← ______________

٩ سمع (هي) ← ______________

١٠ فعل (أنا) ← ______________

4 Read about the three people below and write notes in the table, as in the examples.

وَحيد مُراسل لجريدة سوريّة. أمس صباحاً ذهب إلى مكتب الجريدة وكتب عن سَرِقة في بنك كبير. رجع إلى البيت مساءً وجلس مع زَوجته. أكل سمكاً وشرب قهوة.

ماري مُمرّضة . أمس ذهبَت إلى المستشفى صباحاً وبعد ذلك ذهبَت إلى السوق. رجعَت إلى البيت مساءً وكتبَت خِطاباً لأُختها. أكلَت فلافل وشربَت فنجان شاي.

وَردة تِلميذة. أمس ذهبَت إلى المدرسة صباحاً وبعد ذلك ذهبَت إلى بيت صاحِبَتها. رجعَت مساءً وفَتَحَت زجاجة كولا وجلسَت أمام التليفزيون. أكلَت بيتزا.

NAME	OCCUPATION	YESTERDAY			
		did what in day?	did what pm?	ate what?	drank what?
Waheed	correspondent	went to office wrote about theft			

5 Yusuf has written another email to his mother about a trip he made yesterday to the town of Sidon (صيدا ṣaydā). Read the email and answer the questions in English.

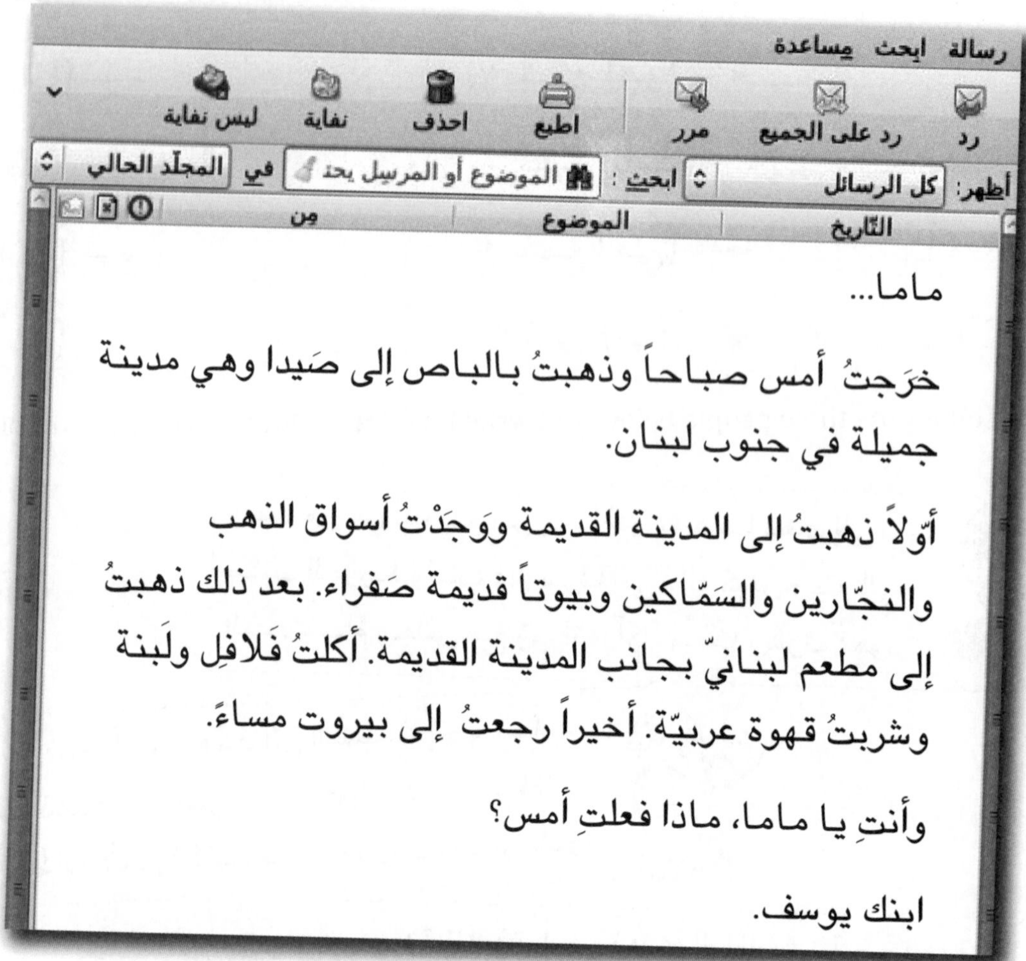

ماما...

خَرَجتُ أمس صباحاً وذهبتُ بالباص إلى صَيدا وهي مدينة جميلة في جنوب لبنان.

أوّلاً ذهبتُ إلى المدينة القديمة ووَجَدْتُ أسواق الذهب والنجّارين والسَمّاكين وبيوتاً قديمة صَفراء. بعد ذلك ذهبتُ إلى مطعم لبنانيّ بجانب المدينة القديمة. أكلتُ فَلافِل ولَبنة وشربتُ قهوة عربيّة. أخيراً رجعتُ إلى بيروت مساءً.

وأنتِ يا ماما، ماذا فعلتِ أمس؟

ابنك يوسف.

1 Where is Sidon?

2 How did Yusuf get there?

3 Where did he go first in Sidon?

4 How many markets did he find in the old city?

5 What type of markets were they?

6 What else did he see in the old city?

7 Where did he go after that?

8 What did he eat and drink?

9 When did he return to Beirut?

10 What question does he ask his mother at the end of the email?

6 Here is a description of what Yusuf did in Sidon. Without looking at the email on page 52, see if you can fill in the gaps in the description, as in the example.

خَرَجَ يوسف أمس __صباحاً__ وذَهَبَ بالباص __________ صَيدا،

وهي مدينة جميلة في __________ لبنان.

أَوّلاً ذهب إلى __________ القديمة وَوجَدَ __________ الذهب

والخبّازين والسَمّاكين وبيوتاً قديمة صَفراء. بعد __________

ذهب إلى مطعم لبنانيّ و __________ فَلافِل ولَبنة و __________

قهوة عربيّة. __________ رجع إلى بيروت __________.

7 **Conversation**

An Arabic-speaking friend, Tamer, is asking you about what you did yesterday.
Prepare your half of the conversation with him and try saying it out loud.
Use the English prompts to guide you, as usual.

تامر: ماذا فعلت أمس؟ mādhā faɛalta(-ti) ams?

أنت: *I went to the gold market.* __________

تامر: وماذا وجدت؟ wa-mādhā wajadta(-ti)?

أنت: *I found a necklace for my sister.* __________

تامر: أين أكلت؟ ayna alkalta(-ti)?

أنت: *I ate in a Lebanese restaurant.* __________

تامر: جميل! وبعد ذلك؟ jamīl! wa-baɛda dhālik?

أنت: *I drank Arabic coffee.* __________

تامر: وهل خرجت مساءً؟ wa-hal kharajta(-ti) masā'an?

أنت: *No, I wrote email[s] to my friends.* __________

unit 13

Wish you were here

1 Identify the root letters of the word on the right and then fill in its meaning and plural.

plural	*meaning*	*root letters*	*word*
كِلاب	dog	ك/ل/ب	كَلب
			رَجُل
			صورة
			جَبَل
			لُعبة
			غُرفة
			بَحر
			جَمَل
			عُلبة

2 Arrange these Arabic numbers from the smallest to the largest.

a سبعة وأربعين
b أحد عشر
c ستّة عشر
d مئة وثلاثة
e مئة وثلاثين
f أربعة
g ثمانية وثلاثين
h اثنا عشر
i ثلاثة وعشرين
j ستّة وستّين
k خمسة عشر
l واحد وخمسين
m تسعة
n أربعين

f, ____

3 أمس ذهبنا إلى السوق.. Yesterday we went to market...

Describe what you found in a crowded market, as in the example.

٧		وجدنا سبعة جمال.	٣		______
٤		______	٣٣		______
١٠		______	١٥		______
٦		______	٥٠		______
٢٠		______	٨٦		______
١٤		______	٩		______

Tip: When writing Arabic numbers you will particularly impress if you can remember:

- the plural is used only after numbers 3–10; 11 and upwards are followed by the *singular*
- the tā' marbūṭa (ة) is removed from numbers 3–10 when counting *feminine* nouns
- after numbers 11–99, the extra alif (اً) is added to the singular noun (unless ending in ة)

ثلاثة رِجال (three men) ثلاثين رَجُلاً (thirty men)

ثلاث غُرَف (three rooms) ثلاثين غُرفة (thirty rooms)

4 Read the card from Iman to her sister Safa and choose the correct word to complete the sentences below, as in the example.

القَلعة القديمة، حمامات، تونس

عزيزتي صفاء،

نحن في مدينة حمّامات في تونس والطقس حارّ جدّاً. درجة الحرارة أربعون! وجدنا فندقاً جميلاً في الشمال الشرقيّ بجانب البحر. وراء الفندق هناك شجر وجبال.

أمس ذهبنا أنا والأولاد إلى القَلعة القديمة ولكن آدَم كتب إيميل في الغُرفة. بعد ذلك أكلنا سمكاً بالكُسكُس في مطعم تونسيّ.

أخيراً ذهبتُ أنا إلى السوق ولكن آدَم والأولاد رجعوا إلى الفندق.

مع تحياتي، أختك إيمان

١ إيمان في...	مصر	(تونس)	فرنسا
٢ الطقس...	بارد	مُعتدل	حارّ
٣ درجة الحرارة...	٢٠	٣٠	٤٠
٤ الفندق بجانب...	البحر	المتحف	السوق
٥ أمس ذهبوا إلى...	القصر	القلعة	البحر
٦ في المطعم أكلوا...	دجاجة	سمكاً	بيتزا
٧ ذهبَت إيمان إلى...	السوق	البنك	المستشفى
٨ ولكن آدَم والأولاد رجعوا إلى...	القلعة	البيت	الفندق

5 Now find the Arabic equivalents of these expressions in the postcard, as in the example.

١ Dear Safa ______ عزيزتي صفاء

٢ very hot ______

٣ in the north-east ______

٤ trees and mountains ______

٥ the boys and I ______

٦ the old fort ______

٧ fish with couscous ______

٨ with my best wishes ______

6 **Conversation**

You are on holiday with your family in France and are talking to your friend, Tamer, over the internet.

أنت: *We're in the town of Avignon.* nahnu fī madīnat afīnyūn.. نحن في مدينة أفينيون

تامر: كيف حال الطقس؟ kayfa ḥāl aṭ-ṭaqṣ?

أنت: *The weather's cold. It's 15°.* ______

تامر: هل أنتم في فندق؟ hal antum fī funduq?

أنت: *No, we found a house in the old town.* ______

تامر: ماذا فعلتُم؟ mādhā faʿaltum?

أنت: *Yesterday we went to the old palace...* ______

and we sat beside the river. ______

تامر: جميل! jamīl!

أنت: *What did you do yesterday, Tamer?* ______

unit 14 All the President's men

1 Put the days of the week in order starting with *Saturday*, as in the example.

❑ يوم الثُلاثاء　　❑ يوم الإثنَين　　❑ يوم الجُمعة

❑ يوم الخَميس　　❑ يوم الأَربِعاء　　❑ يوم الأَحد

١ يوم السَّبت

2 Look at the pictures of what Tariq did last week, and then fill in the table below.

يوم الأسبوع	الصورة	ماذا فعل طارق؟
الثلاثاء	٢	حضر معرض صُوَر.
		أكل في مطعم إيرانيّ.
		ذهب إلى البنك صباحاً.
		كتب إيميل لِابن أخته.
		شرب قهوة في بيت صاحبه.
		لعب مع الكلب.
		جلس مع أمّه.

3 Complete this table of words with similar root patterns and give their meanings, as in the example.

plural فعلاء	*person* فعيل	*noun* فعالة	*root letters*
سُفَراء ambassadors	سَفير ambassador	سِفارة embassy	س/ف/ر
			و/ز/ر
			و/ك/ل
			ز/ع/م
			ر/ء/س
			ء/م/ر

4 Put the Arabic business and political vocabulary into the word grid. The shaded squares will then spell out another item of vocabulary vertically. One is completed for you.

~~exhibition~~ meeting conference agency embassy council ministry

			ت					
						ك		
			ف					
							ز	
		ض	ر	ع	م			
ر								
			س					

Additional vocabulary = ______________________

5 Match the pictures to the government department, as in the example.

١ التَّعليم

٢ الخارِجيّة

٣ الثَّقافة

٤ العَدل

٥ الصِّناعة

٦ الصِّحّة

٧ الدِفاع

٨ الدّاخِلِيّة

٩ الاِقتِصاد

١٠ الزِراعة

a 

b 

c 

d 

e 

f 

g 

h 

i 

j 

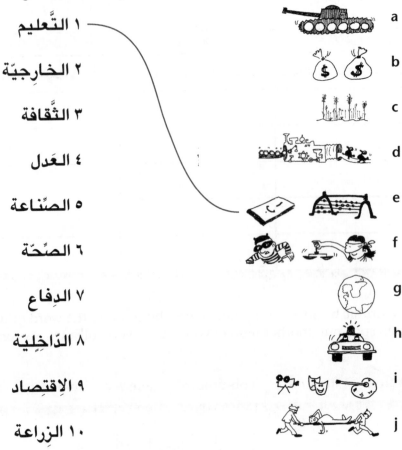

6 Now make adjectives from the nouns below, as in the example.

١ تَعليم (education) ← تعليميّ (educational)

٢ زِراعة (agriculture) ← ____________

٣ دِفاع (defence) ← ____________

٤ إقتصاد (economy) ← ____________

٥ صِناعة (industry) ← ____________

٦ حُكومة (government) ← ____________

٧ ثَقافة (culture) ← ____________

٨ صِحّة (health) ← ____________

7 Match the two halves of the sentences, for example ١d.

١ حضر السفير... | a لِوزير التعليم.
٢ جلسَت وزيرة الصحّة مع... | b الصناعة مؤتمراً للمهندسين.
٣ كَتبَت المدرّسة خطاباً... | c الإمارات يوم الأحد.
٤ هل لعبتِ... | d جلسة مع الملك السعوديّ.
٥ أمس ذهبتُ... | e الوزراء اجتماعاً يوم السبت.
٦ فتحتُ الزجاجة... | f عن السرقة في الفندق؟
٧ حضر وزير... | g الممرّضات في المستشفى.
٨ هل سَمِعْتَ... | h إلى السفارة الفرنسيّة.
٩ عقد رئيس... | i باللُعَب الجديدة في المعرض؟
١٠ رجعوا من... | j وشربتُ الماء البارد.

8 **Conversation**

You are talking to your friend, Abdullah, about a conference you attended last Thursday.

عبد الله: ماذا فعلت الخميس؟ mādhā faعalta(-ti) il-khamīs?

أنت: *I went to the Ministry of Industry.* ____________________

عبد الله: لماذا؟ li-mādhā?

أنت: *I attended a large conference...* ____________________

عبد الله: مع من؟ maعa man?

أنت: *with engineers from the Middle East.* ____________________

عبد الله: ما شاء الله! mā shā' allāh!

أنت: *The Prime Minister attended the opening.* ____________________

عبد الله: رئيس الوزراء؟ ra'īs al-wuzarā'?

أنت: *Yes, and I sat next to him!* ____________________

unit 15 Review

1 Describe how many of each item there are in the toy shop window, as in the example.

في الشبّاك هناك خمسة جمال، ثلاثة...

2 Complete the crossword in English using the Arabic clues. One clue is completed for you.

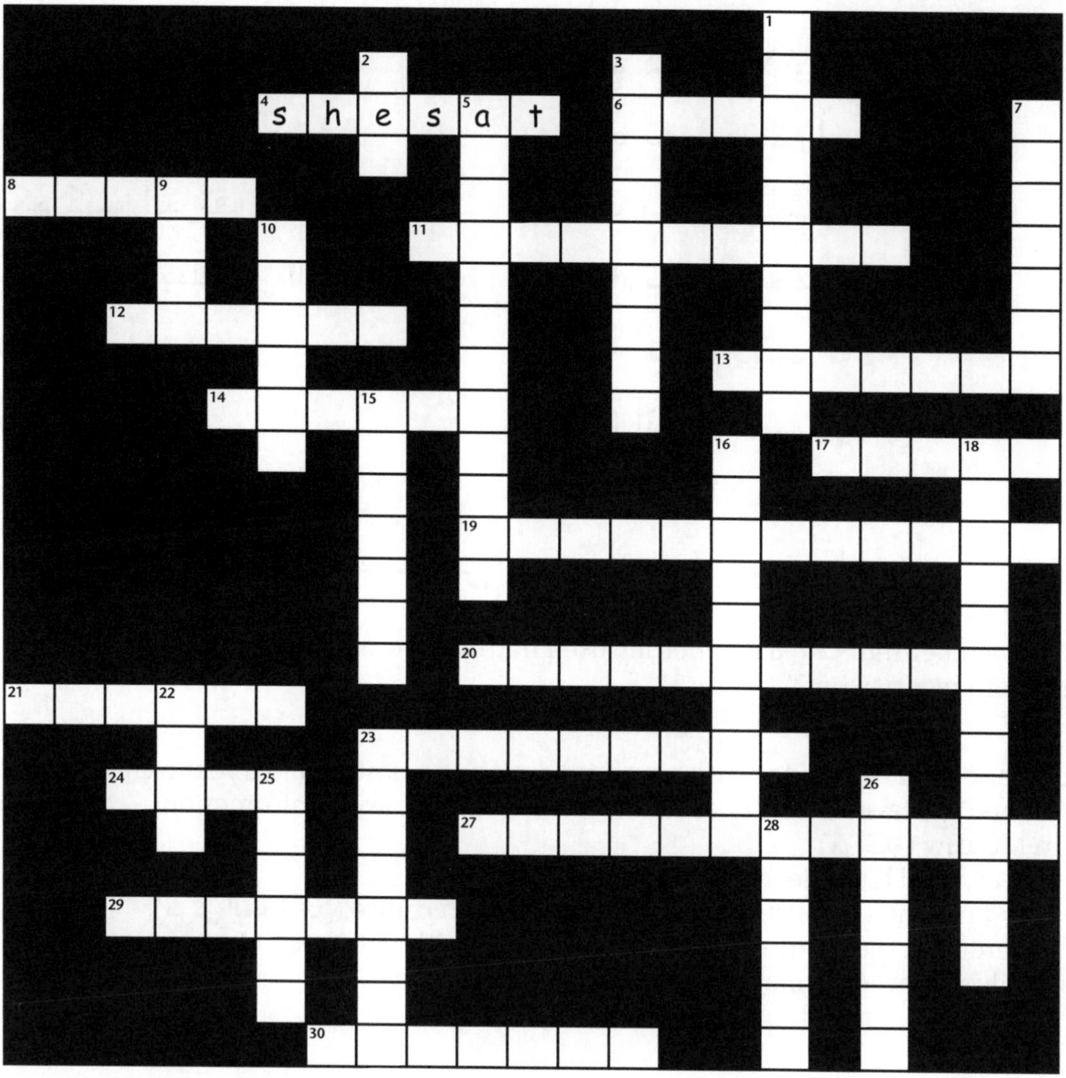

Across

4 جَلَسَت (3,3)
6 ثمانية (5)
8 أسوَد (5)
11 خاتم فضّة (6,4)
12 شَرِبتُ (1,5)
13 زُجاجات (6)
14 ذَهبنا (2,4)
17 جَنوب (5)
19 فِنجان قهوة (1,3,2,6)
20 تحت السرير (5,3,3)
21 يوم الإثنَين (6)
23 وُزَراء (9)
24 أكواب [بلاستيك] (4)
27 رَجَعوا (4,8)
29 كَتَبَ (2,5)
30 إنجليزيّ (7)

Down

1 مَعرِض (10)
2 أحمَر (3)
3 أمس (9)
5 زِراعيّ (12)
7 شُموع (7)
9 بارِد (4)
10 أطباق (6)
15 سِفارة (7)
16 ثلاثة وخمسين (5-5)
18 الشَّرق الأوسَط (3,6,4)
22 طَبلة (4)
23 جبَل (8)
25 سُيوف (6)
26 بُرتقال (7)
28 ثلاثين (6)

3 Match the questions to the answers, for example ١f.

١ ما عملك؟	a هناك ثلاثين.
٢ متى وصلتَ إلى دِمشَق؟	b نعم. كتبتُه أمس.
٣ بكم كيلو البرتقال؟	c نحن من شمال لبنان.
٤ ماذا وجد ابنك في الشارع؟	d بخير، الحمد الله.
٥ أنتم من أين؟	e خاتم ذهب!
٦ كيف حالك؟	f أنا مهندس زراعيّ.
٧ هل كتبتِ الإيميل للوزير؟	g يوم الأحد.
٨ هناك كم ممرّضة في المستشفى؟	h بعشرة جنيهات.

Tip: Remember that ما mā is generally used in front of a noun and ماذا mādhā in front of a verb; both mean 'what?'

4 Imagine you are on holiday with your friends. Write a postcard to a relative based on the model and expressions on pages 56–57. Include the following information:

- in Moscow (موسكو)
- it's very cold (zero degrees)
- found new hotel – north-west next to exhibition centre (مَركَز المَعارِض)
- yesterday: large palace in centre of town/fish with potatoes in Russian restaurant
- finally: you went to museum/friends returned to hotel

5 How do you say these in Arabic?

1 I found the key under the chair. وجدتُ المفتاح تحت الكرسيّ.

2 The weather is very hot in Oman. ______

3 We attended a party in the embassy. ______

4 Did you *(plural)* go to the museum? ______

5 They arrived on Sunday. ______

6 I sat on the black chair near the door. ______

6 **Conversation**

Your friend Amira is taking you for a ride in her new car. You are asking her about a small bag she lost yesterday. Follow the prompts as usual to join in the conversation. (Note: seat = مقعد miqعad)

أنت: *Did you find your bag?* ______

أميرة: لا. lā.

أنت: *Where did you go yesterday?* ______

أميرة: ذهبتُ إلى المطعم الجديد. dhahabtu ilā l-maṭعam il-jadīd.

أنت: *Where did you sit in the restaurant?* ______

أميرة: بجانب الباب. bi-jānib al-bāb.

أنت: *And how did you return to the house?* ______

أميرة: بسيّارتي. bi-sayyāratī.

أنت: *Ahh... Is your bag black?* ______

أميرة: نعم! هل وجدتُها؟ naعam! hal wajadtahā?

أنت: *Yes, between the seat and the door!* ______

unit 16 Every day

1 كم الساعة؟. Write out the correct time, as in the example.

١  الساعة الثالثة

٢ 

٣ 

٤ 

٥ 

٦ 

٧ 

٨ 

٩ 

١٠ 

2 Sami is a mechanical engineer. Look at his work-day routine; then fill in the gaps in the paragraph using the information from the pictures, as in the example.

سامي مهندس ميكانيكيّ. كلّ يوم **يغسل** وَجهَهُ الساعة ________ ويَلبِس

مَلابِس العمل. ثُمّ ________ الإفطار الساعة السادسة و ________. يَخرُج من

البيت ________ السابعة ويَذهَب إلى مَصنَع السيّارات بالـ________. يَرجَع

من ________ إلى البيت الساعة ________ والرُّبع ويَرسِم صُوَراً للشَّجَر والجِبال

والأنهار بالألوان. يأكل ________ الساعة الثامنة إلا ________ وبعد ذلك

يَشرَب ________ شاي. أخيراً ________ البيجاما ويَنام الساعة ________.

Tip: ملابس malābis = clothes; ينام yanām = he sleeps

3 Match the Arabic school and university subjects to the English equivalents, for example **١e**.

sport **a**	١ الجُغرافيا
history **b**	٢ الرِّياضة
Arabic **c**	٣ الموسيقى
engineering **d**	٤ الطِبّ
geography **e**	٥ الإنجليزيّة
drawing/art **f**	٦ التَربية الدينيّة
law **g**	٧ الرِّياضيّات
chemistry **h**	٨ الرَّسم
music **i**	٩ الهَندَسة
English **j**	١٠ الكيمياء
medicine **k**	١١ الحُقوق
mathematics **l**	١٢ العربيّة
religious education **m**	١٣ التاريخ

4 Look at this school timetable and describe the pupils' day, as in the example.

١ يدرُسون الجغرافيا من الساعة التاسعة حتّى العاشرة إلا رُبعاً.

٢ ____________________

٣ ____________________

٤ ____________________

٥ ____________________

٦ ____________________

5 Change the verbs according to the pronoun in brackets, as in the example.
Then choose from the verbs you have written to complete the five sentences below.

١ يَذهَب (هي) ← تَذهَب (she goes)	٥ يأكُل (أنتِ) ← ________
٢ يشرَب (أنا) ← ________	٦ يَحضُر (أنتَ) ← ________
٣ يَدرُس (هم) ← ________	٧ يَلبَس (أنتم) ← ________
٤ يَغسِل (نحن) ← ________	٨ يَكتُب (هم) ← ________

يا أولاد، هل ________ البيجامات؟

كلّ يوم أنا وأخي ________ الأطباق بعد العشاء.

بعد الغداء أجلس في كرسيّ و________ فنجان قهوة.

هم ________ التاريخ من الساعة التاسعة حتّى الساعة العاشرة.

لماذا لا ________ المُحاضرات في الجامعة، يا أحمد؟

6 **Conversation**

You are talking to Ali about your everyday routine.

علي: ماذا تفعل(ين) كلّ اليوم؟ mādhā tafعal(-īna) kull yawm?

أنت: *We eat breakfast at 8 o'clock...* ________

and I leave the house at 8:30. ________

علي: كيف تذهب(ين) إلى المكتب؟ kayfa tadh-hab(-īna) ilā l-maktab?

أنت: *I go to the centre of town by train...* ________

then I go by bus to the office. ________

علي: وفي المساء؟ wa fīl-masā'?

أنت: *I return at 5:30 or 5:45...* ________

and we eat dinner at 7:30. ________

And you? What do you do every day? ________

unit 17

Eating and drinking

1 Find the food-related words in the word square. The words can read right to left or top to bottom. One is completed for you.

ل	ا	ق	ت	ر	ب	ث	ف	ز	ك	س	ع
و	ن	ب	ي	ه	ة	م	ع	ط	م	ا	س
ك	خ	س	م	ص	ي	ا	ن	و	ك	ظ	ي
ا	(ر	ك	س)	ا	ش	ض	ل	ز	ر	أ	ر
ة	ظ	و	م	ل	ا	ك	ب	ج	و	ل	ح
ؤ	ل	ي	ط	ش	ي	ه	د	ة	ن	ب	ج
ن	ي	ت	ا	ي	ذ	ص	ر	غ	ة	ف	ع
ة	ز	ع	ط	س	ج	ك	ع	ك	س	ي	ب
ز	و	م	ذ	خ	ر	و	د	م	و	ث	ي
ي	ة	ض	ي	ب	ي	ل	ح	غ	ا	ن	ض
ت	ز	ب	ق	ز	ك	ا	ن	ي	ط	ب	ك
ل	ا	ق	ب	ه	ذ	ح	ة	ر	ي	ص	ع

~~sugar~~	eggs
tea	juice
macaroni	grocer
rice	cola
cheese	milk
restaurant	bread
oranges	figs
biscuits	bananas
cake	oil

2 Now choose a suitable container or measure for each food item, as in the example.

١ زُجاجة / (كيس) سكّر

٢ كيلو / لِتر بطاطس

٣ زجاجة / قِطعة جبنة

٤ عُلبة / أنبوبة مكرونة

٥ لِتر / علبة بيض

٦ نصف لِتر / قِطعة حليب

٧ زجاجة / أنبوبة زَيت

٨ نصف كيلو / لِتر عصير تفّاح

٩ رُبع لِتر / رُبع كيلو بُنّ

١٠ أنبوبة / كيس مَعجون طماطم

3 Jamila is doing her weekly shop in the local grocery. Look at her shopping list and complete the conversation with the grocer, as in the example.

٣ عُلَب بسكويت
زجاجة عصير برتقال
نصف كيلو جبنة بيضاء
كيس سكّر
كيلو تفّاح أخضر
أنبوبة معجون أسنان
علبة مسحوق غسيل

البقّال: صباح الخير يا مدام.

جميلة: صباح النور. أعطِني من فضلك ثلاث عُلَب بسكويت و________ عصير.

البقّال: عصير تفاح؟

جميلة: لا، عصير ________ من فضلك. وأريد نصف كيلو ________ بيضاء.

البقّال: تفضّلي. شيء ثاني؟

جميلة: ________ سكّر وكيلو ________ أخضر.

البقّال: تحت أمرك.

جميلة: وهل عندكم معجون ________ و________ غسيل؟

البقّال: عندنا ________ غسيل يا مدام ولكن ليس عندنا معجون ________ .

جميلة: طيِّب... علبة ________ غسيل من فضلك. كم الحساب؟

البقّال: خمسة وأربعين جنيهاً.

جميلة: تفضّل. مع السلامة.

Which item on her list did Jamila not manage to buy? And how much was the bill?

4 The verbs below are all useful for talking about food and household tasks. Complete the table, as in the example.

verb form	root	meaning	present verb	past verb
Form II	ن/ظ/ف	to clean	يُنَظِّف	نَظَّف
				سَخَّن
				طَبَخ
				جَهَّز
				أَخْرَج
				جَرَّب
				عاوَن
				رَتَّب
				حَجَز

5 Maha has been away for the weekend and has come back to find the house in chaos. Her husband is telling her the family have completed their chores but Maha disagrees! Play the part of Maha and contradict all his claims, as in the example.

١ نَظَّفَ أحمد المَطبَخ. لا! لَم يُنَظِّف المطبخ! (No! He didn't clean the kitchen!)

٢ جَهَّزَتْ سارة السَلَطة. ______

٣ أخرَجَ جمال الزُبالة. ______

٤ سَخَّنتُ الخُبز. ______

٥ طَبَخنا السمك. ______

٦ حَجَزتُ المَطعَم. ______

٧ عاوَنَتْني راندا. ______

٨ رَتَّبوا غُرَفهُم. ______

Tip: Past negative = لم lam + *present tense* (without any final ن nūn):
(لم يذهب lam yadh-hab, he didn't go; لم يعاونوا lam yuɛāwinū, they didn't help)

6 Shorten the sentences using the appropriate ending, as in the example.

١ صَلَّحتُ السيّارة. (I fixed the car.) ← صلّحتُها (I fixed it.) ________

٢ سَخَّنتُ الخبز ← ________

٣ أخرَجنا الزبالة. ← ________

٤ كلّ يوم تُجَهِّز فاطمة السلطة. ← ________

٥ كلّ يوم يُنَظِّف منير المطبخ. ← ________

٦ هل غَسَلتِ الأطباق؟ ← ________

٧ هل أَخَذتَ الأولاد إلى المدرسة؟ ← ________

7 **Conversation**

You are in a restaurant ordering a meal. Follow the prompts to order from the waiter.
(Note: rice pudding = أرزّ بالحليب aruzz bil-ḥalīb, literally 'rice with milk')

أنت: *I booked a table yesterday.* ________

الجرسون: الاسم من فضلك؟ al-ism min faḍlak(-ik)?

أنت: *The name is Reed.* ________

الجرسون: نعم، المائدة جاهزة... naɛam, al-mā'ida jāhiza...

أنت: *Waiter! One chicken with rice, please.* ________

الجرسون: تحت أمرك. taḥt amrak(-ik)

أنت: *And I'd like the tomato salad.* ________

الجرسون: والمشروب؟ wal-mashrūb?

أنت: *I'll have a cold orange juice.* ________

الجرسون: هل تجرّب الحلويات بعد ذلك؟ hal tujarrib al-ḥalawīyyāt baɛda dhālik?

أنت: *Yes. I'll have the rice pudding.* ________

الجرسون: تحت أمرك. taḥt amrak(-ik)

unit 18

Comparing things

1 Identify the root letters of the adjective on the right and then fill in the comparative word with its meaning. (Note: سعيد saعīd = happy)

meaning	*comparative*	*root letters*	*adjective*
bigger/larger	أَكْبَر	ك/ب/ر	كبير
			صغير
			جميل
			رخيص
			بارد
			قصير
			سَعيد
			سريع
			ثقيل
			جديد
			خفيف
			غَنيّ
			هامّ
			قَويّ
			حُلو

Tip: In the comparative, doubled (identical second and third) root letters are written together (خفيف khafīf/أخفّ akhaff, light/lighter), and final root letters و or ي are written as alif maqṣūra (غنيّ ghanī/أغنى aghnā, rich/richer).

2 Samira has a neighbour called Nadia who loves to boast! She always wants to go one better than Samira and have the biggest and best of everything in the street. You play the part of Nadia (ن) and respond to what Samira (س) says, as in the example.

س: بَيتي كبير. ن: بيتي أكبر من بيتك. هو أكبر بيت في الشارع!

س: اِبني طويل. ن: ....

س: بِنتي جميلة. ن: ....

س: خاتمي قديم. ن: ....

س: سيّارتي سريعة. ن: ....

س: درّاجتي جديدة. ن: ....

س: حقيبتي خفيفة. ن: ....

س: مشروبي بارد. ن: ....

س: عصيري حُلو. ن: ....

س: زوجي غنيّ. ن: ....

س: اِجتِماعي هامّ. ن: ....

س: قِلادتي غالية. ن: ....

3 Read the magazine profile of a prominent businessman, Mohammed Abbas, and answer the questions. There may be a few unfamiliar words but try to get the gist.

Tip: Remember to start with the right-hand column.

1 What was Mohammed's father's profession and working hours?
2 How many rooms did the family house have?
3 What days did Mohammed help his father?
4 Was Mohammed well-off as a boy? What about now?
5 What does he own and where are they?
6 Where does he live now and with whom?
7 Was Mohammed happy as a boy? How does he describe his parents?
8 What does he still do today in the morning that he did as a boy?

مُنذُ ثلاثين سنة كان محمّد عبّاس ولداً فقيراً. أبوه، الشيخ عبّاس، كان خبّازاً صغيراً يَعمَل في مَخبَزه كلّ يوم من الساعة الرابعة صباحاً حتّى الساعة السابعة مساءً. كان لَهُم بَيت صغير من غُرفَتَين: غُرفة للوالدَين وغُرفة للأولاد السبعة.

كان محمد أكبر ولد، ولذلك كان يعاون والده في المخبز أيام الخميس والجمعة والسبت.

هذا الولد الفقير هو الآن رَجُل لَهُ أكثر من تسعين مخبزاً في الشرق الأوسط. بيته قصر جميل وكبير بجانب النهر، يَعيش فيه مع زوجته وأولاده.

يَقول محمد عبّاس «نعم، أنا كُنتُ فقيراً، ولكنّي كنتُ سَعيداً. أبي كان رَجُلاً قَويّاً وتَعَلَّمتُ مِنه حُبّ العمل. وأمّي كانت كريمة وجميلة وكانت أفضل طبّاخة في الشارع! كُنّا فُقَراء، ولكن كنّا نأكل خُبزاً دافِئاً مع قِطعة جُبنة كلّ صباح.»

محمّد عبّاس هو اليوم أهمّ وأغنى رجل في المدينة، له أشهَر مَخابِز في العالَم العربيّ وإلى اليوم يأكل كلّ صباح خبزاً دافئاً وقِطعة جُبنة لِلإفطار مع أولاده.

4 In the article find the Arabic for the words and expressions below, as in the example.

١ bakery/bakeries مَخبَز / مَخابِز
٢ for the [two] parents ______
٣ and for that [reason] ______
٤ his parent (father) ______
٥ he lives ______
٦ I was happy ______
٧ the love of work ______
٨ warm bread ______
٩ most famous ______
١٠ until today ______

5 Rewrite these sentences in the past, as in the example.

١ أنا في البنك. كُنتُ في البنك.

٢ هُم في المصنع. ______

٣ هي طبّاخة. ______

٤ هل أنتَ الأطوَل؟ ______

٥ هو وزير. ______

٦ الغُرفة جميلة. ______

٧ نحن فُقَراء. ______

٨ هل أنتِ سعيدة؟ ______

٩ الأطباق جديدة. ______

١٠ هل أنتُم أصحاب؟ ______

6 **Conversation**

You are reminiscing with your friend Anwar about your grandfather (جدّ jadd) and grandmother (جدّة jadda).

أنت: *I remember my grandfather.* ______

أنور: ماذا كان عمله؟ mādhā kāna ɛamaluh?

أنت: *40 years ago, he was an actor.* ______

أنور: في السينما؟ fī s-sīnimā?

أنت: *Yes, he was a famous actor.* ______

I learnt from him the love of films. ______

أنور: وماذا عن جدّتك؟ wa-mādhā ɛan jaddatak(ik)?

أنت: *She was the best cook!* ______

Her desserts were delicious. ______

أنور: يا سلام! yā salām!

أنت: *I was the happiest child (طِفل) in the street!* ______

unit

19 Future plans

1 Put the months of the year in order starting with *January*, as in the example.

☐ أبريل	☐ فَبراير	☐ ديسمبر
☐ أغُسطُس	☐ يونيو	☐ مايو
١ يَنايِر	☐ نوفمبِر	☐ مارِس
☐ أُكتوبِر	☐ يوليو	☐ سَبتَمبِر

2 Now write the day and date shown on the calendar, as in the example.

١ يوم الخميس، ١٥ يناير

٢ ______

٣ ______

٤ ______

٥ ______

٦ ______

٧ ______

٨ ______

3 A tour guide is telling her group what they will be doing the next day in Luxor (**الأقصر** al-aqṣur). Read what she says and complete the itinerary.
(Note: **معبد** maعbad = temple; **وادي** wādī = valley)

غداً سَتَزورون الأَقصر. الإفطار الساعة الخامسة والثُلث
صباحاً وسنأخذ الباص الساعة السادسة إلى وادي المُلوك غَرب النهر.
بعد ثلاث ساعات في وادي الملوك سنذهب إلى المتحف الفِرعونيّ في وسط المدينة.
الغداء في مطعم «آمون» بجانب مَعبَد الكَرنَك المشهور، وبعد الغداء
سَتَزورون المعبد. سنرجع إلى الفندق للعشاء الساعة الثامنة.

Wonders of the Nile عجائب النيل

Day 6: Luxor يوم ٦: الأقصر

Breakfast at __________ **AM**

Leave hotel at __________ **AM**

Visits:

1 ______________________________

2 ______________________________

(*Lunch:* __________ *Restaurant*)

3 ______________________________

Return to hotel at __________ **PM**

4 Basma has a busy day tomorrow. She has written down everything she needs to do so that she doesn't forget. Make sentences about her plans, as in the example.

٩:٣٠ أمّي في المستشفى
١١:٢٠ اجتماع في المدرسة
١٣:٠٠ غداء مع مُنيرة
١٤:١٥ إلى البقّال
١٦:٠٠ إيميل للبنك
١٧:٠٠ غسل الملابس
١٨:٣٠ طبخ اللحم للعشاء

١ سَتَزور أمّها في المستشفى الساعة التاسعة والنصف.

٢ ______

٣ ______

٤ ______

٥ ______

٦ ______

٧ ______

5 Choose one of the future verbs in the box to complete each sentence, as in the example.

سَتأكُل سَندرُس سَأرجَع سَيسافِر ~~سَيحضُر~~
سَيزورون سَتُغادِرين سَتُقلِع سَتَستغرِق

١ غدا سَيَحضُر الوزير اِجتماعاً في القصر الملكيّ.

٢ بعد غَد ______ إلى بيتي مع زوجتي.

٣ ______ التاريخ الفرنسيّ في جامعة باريس.

٤ ______ الطائرة الساعة السادسة والنصف صباحاً.

٥ هل ______ في المطعم الجديد يا أحمد؟

٦ الرِحلة من عمّان إلى البَتراء *(Petra)* ______ ثلاث ساعات.

٧ ______ الأولاد إلى القاهرة و______ المتحف المصريّ.

٨ متى ______ سوريا، يا سميرة؟

6 You are going on an extended study and leisure visit to Syria and Jordan. Write a note to a friend telling him or her about your plans. Include the following information:

- January 3: travel to Damascus (plane takes off 4AM!)
- January and February: Study Arabic in Damascus University.
- March: Leave Syria. Travel by bus to Jordan.
- Visit friends in Amman. Go to Petra.
- April: finally return home.

7 **Conversation**

You are on holiday in Egypt and your friend, Adam, is asking you about your plans for the next couple of days.

آدم: ماذا ستفعلون غداً وبعد غد؟ mādhā sa-tafـعalūna ghadan wa-baـعda ghad?

أنت: *Tomorrow we'll travel to Luxor by train.* ______

آدم: هل الرحلة طويلة؟ hal ar-riḥla ṭawīla?

أنت: *Yes, it will take nine hours.* ______

آدم: أين ستنامون؟ ayna sa-tanāmūna?

أنت: *We'll sleep on ('in') the train.* ______

آدم: وماذا ستفعلون في الأقصر؟ wa-mādhā sa-tafـعalūna fīl-aqṣur?

أنت: *On Saturday we'll visit the Valley of the Kings.* ______

أنت: *And we'll go to Karnak temple on Sunday.* ______

آدم: جميل! رحلة سعيدة! jamīl! riḥla saـعīda!

unit 20 Review

1 Complete the table of verbs, as in the example.

verb form	*root*	*meaning*	*present verb*	*past verb*
Form V	ح/د/ث	to talk	يَتَحَدَّث	تَحَدَّث
				غادَر
				أَقْلَع
				تَذَكَّر
				اِجْتَمَع
				اِسْتَغرَق
				تَعاوَن
				تَعَلَّم
				اِنْطَلَق

2 Now complete each sentence with one of the verbs above in the correct form.

١ الرِحلة إلى الفندق ________ (will last) خمس ساعات.

٢ ذهبنا إلى المطعم بعد أن ________ (left) السينما.

٣ ________ (talks) بسمة مع أُمّها على التِليفون كلّ يوم.

٤ هل أنتَ ________ (remember) رحلتنا إلى الأقصر مع المدرسة؟

٥ الرِجال ________ (cooperated) وأخذوا العُلَب الثقيلة من السيّارة.

٦ أمس، ________ (took off) طائرتي وأنا في التاكسي!

3 Complete the crossword in English using the Arabic clues. One clue is completed for you.

Across

4 نغسل (2,4)

6 الأكبر في العالم (3,7,2,3,5)

7 تعاونوا (4,10)

10 رياضة (5)

12 شهر (5)

14 بالقطار (2,5)

15 نتذكّر (2,8)

17 أغنى من الملك (6,4,3,4)

19 متى؟ (4)

23 يلعبون (4,4)

24 موسيقى (5)

25 أدرس (1,5)

26 روسيا (6)

Down

1 غداء (5)

2 هامّ (9)

3 الساعة الرابعة والنصف (4,4,4)

5 قطعة جبنة (1,5,2,6)

8 كانوا (4,4)

9 مطاعم (11)

11 كلّ يوم (6,3)

13 غداً (8)

15 سنزور (2,4,5)

16 محاضرة (7)

18 معجون أسنان (10)

20 نوفمبر (8)

21 لحم (4)

22 مسجد (6)

23 اليوم (5)

4 Make these sentences negative, using لا lā, لم lam or ليس laysa, as in the example.

١ هناك مفتاح لِهذا الباب. ليس هناك مفتاح لِهذا الباب.

٢ أشرب الشاي في المساء. ____________

٣ ذهبَتْ فاطمة إلى مكتبها. ____________

٤ عندنا معجون أسنان. ____________

٥ هناك كلاب في الشارع. ____________

٦ نسمع السيّارات من الشبّاك. ____________

٧ جَرَّبنا الكمبيوتر الجديد في المعرض. ____________

٨ غادرتُم البيت أمس صباحاً. ____________

5 Jamal goes to the grocer with his shopping list. Read his conversation with the grocer and complete the shopping list.

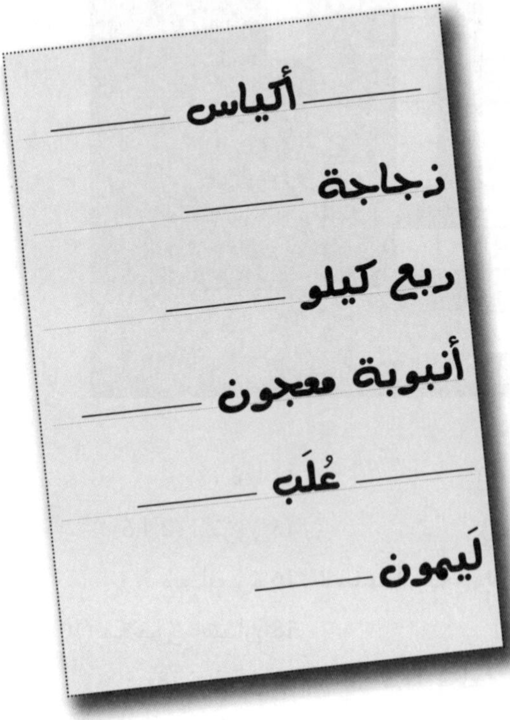

البقّال: صباح الخير يا سيّدي.

جمال: صباح النور. أعطِني من فضلك أربعة أكياس أرزّ وزجاجة زَيت.

البقّال: تفضّل. شيء ثاني؟

جمال: نعم. أريد ربع كيلو بُنّ وأنبوبة معجون طماطم.

البقّال: تحت أمرك.

جمال: وهل عندكم تين ولَيمون أصفر؟

البقّال: عندنا تين يا سيّدي ولكن ليس عندنا لَيمون أصفر... عندنا الأخضر.

جمال: أُفضِّل الأصفر... خمس عُلَب تين من فضلك. كم الحساب؟

البقّال: ثلاثة وستّين جنيهاً.

جمال: تفضّل. مع السلامة.

How much was his bill this week and which item did the grocer not have available?

6 How do you say these in Arabic?

1 I returned from Damascus on Friday. رجعتُ من دمشق يوم الجمعة.

2 We learn Arabic at ('in the') university. ____________

3 We ate meat with Arabic bread. ____________

4 The Nile is the longest river in the world. ____________

5 I'll write you *(masc.)* a letter. ____________

6 I'll talk to Adam tomorrow. ____________

7 **Conversation**

You are back from Luxor and you are telling your friend, Adam, about the rest of your stay, including a visit to the university and mosque of Al-Azhar (الأزهر).

آدم: متى رجعتُم من الأقصر؟ matā rajaعtum min al-aqṣur?

أنت: *We returned from Luxor on Monday.* ____________

And yesterday we visited Al-Azhar. ____________

It's the oldest university in the world. ____________

آدم: نعم، والمسجد جميل. naعam, wal-masjid jamīl.

أنت: *After that, we ate pigeon with Arabic bread. It was delicious!*

____

آدم: ومتى ستُغادرون مصر؟ wa-matā sa-tughādirūna miṣr?

أنت: *Our plane will take off tomorrow at 3am.* ____________

آدم: الساعة الثالثة؟! as-sāعa ath-thālitha?!

أنت: *So I'll say "goodbye" now.* ____________

But I'll study Arabic on the internet... ____________

and I'll write you an email! ____________

Answers to activities

Unit 1 Getting started

Activity 1
3 bu, 7 tha, 6 yu, 10 ya, 1 ba, 9 tu, 4 thi, 8 ni, 2 ti, 5 na

Activity 2

1 نُ	5 يِ
2 تَ	6 ثَ
3 بِ	7 بُ
4 ثُ	8 تُ

Activity 3

at the end	in the middle	at the beginning	letter
ـب	ـبـ	بـ	ب (bā')
ـت	ـتـ	تـ	ت (tā')
ـث	ـثـ	ثـ	ث (thā')
ـن	ـنـ	نـ	ن (nūn)
ـي	ـيـ	يـ	ي (yā')

Activity 4

ثابت البنا وزير التعليم اللبناني
في البيت الأبيض يوم الثلاثاء

ب 5 ت 3 ث 3 ن 3 ي 7

Activity 5
Handwriting practice. *Try to show your handwriting to an Arabic-speaking teacher or friend.*

Activity 6
1b, 2a, 3b, 4c, 5c, 6c, 7a, 8b

Activity 7

1 بَيت
2 تِبن
3 بَينَ
4 بُنّ
5 بِنت

Activity 8

1 صباح النور ṣabāḥ an-nūr
2 مساء النور masā' an-nūr
3 أهلاً بكَ ahlan bik(a)
4 أهلاً بكِ ahlan biki

Unit 2 Putting words together

Activity 1

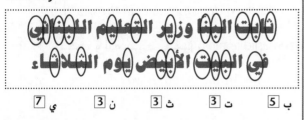

Activity 2

1 نور
2 زين
3 أندي
4 باري
5 زيد
6 أنور
7 داني
8 نادر
9 دينا
10 ثابت

Activity 3

1 دينا وَنور 2 أندي وَزين 3 أنور وَزيد
4 ثابت وَباري 5 نور وَداني 6 باري وَنادر
7 أنور وَدينا 8 نادر وَأندي

Activity 4
Handwriting practice. *Try to show your handwriting to an Arabic-speaking teacher or friend.*

Activity 5
1b, 2a, 3b, 4c, 5a, 6c

Activity 6

1 أنا زيد.

2 أنا نور وأنت؟

3 أنا بدر وأنتَ؟

4 أنا داني.

5 أنتَ أنور؟

6 أنت زينب؟

Activity 7

أنت: أهلاً يا زينب. ahlan yā zaynab.

زينب: أهلاً بك. ahlan bik(i).

أنت: كيف الحال؟ kayf al-ḥāl?

زينب: الحمد لله. al-ḥamdu lillāh.

أنت: أنت أنور؟ anta anwar?

أنور: نعم، أنا أنور. naعam, anā anwar.

أنت: تشرّفنا يا أنور. tasharrafnā yā anwar.

أنور: تشرّفنا. tasharrafnā.

unit 3 The family

Activity 1

1d, 2a, 3f, 4c, 5b, 6e

Activity 2

Handwriting practice. *Try to show your handwriting to an Arabic-speaking teacher or friend.*

Activity 3

ث	ا	ذ	د	ت	ي	ب
ة	ر	خ	م	ر	ه	ن
ج	ب	ي	ت	ي	ذ	ت
ر	ا	م	ح	ذ	ث	ر
ي	ث	ة	ج	ا	ج	د
د	ا	م	ح	ب	م	ه
ة	ج	ا	ج	ز	ي	ذ

1 زُجاجة F

2 بَيت M

3 جَريدة F

4 حِمار M

5 بِنت F

6 خَيمة F

7 دَجاجة F

8 نَهر M

Activity 4

1 أخي 2 أبي 3 أمّي 4 أختي

5 ابني 6 بنتي 7 زوجي 8 زوجتي

9 بيتي 10 مدينتي

Activity 5

1 مها 2 أيمن 3 ماري

4 حامد 5 بدر 6 زيزي

Activity 6

1 هذا زوجي، حامد.

2 هذه أمّي، مها.

3 ماري هي بنت أيمن.

4 نادية هي زوجة حامد.

5 مَن بدر؟ هو ابني.

6 من ماري؟ هي بنتي.

Activity 7

زينب: أهلاً. ahlan.

أنت: كيف الحال يا زينب؟ kayf al-ḥāl yā zaynab?

زينب: الحمد لله. al-ḥamdu lillāh.

أنت: زينب، هذا أبي. zaynab, hādhā abī.

زينب: تشرّفنا. ومن هذه؟ tasharrafnā. wa-man hādhihi?

أنت: هذه ميمي. هي أختي. hādhihi mīmī. hiya ukhtī.

زينب: أهلاً يا ميمي! ahlan yā mīmī!

أنت: آه... هذا هو قطاري. āh... hādhā huwa qiṭārī.

زينب: مع السلامة! maعa s-salāma!

أنت: مع السلامة! maعa s-salāma!

unit 4 Jobs

Activity 1

at the end	*in the middle*	*at the beginning*	*letter*
ـس	ـسـ	سـ	س (sīn)
ـش	ـشـ	شـ	ش (shīn)
ـص	ـصـ	صـ	ص (ṣād)
ـض	ـضـ	ضـ	ض (ḍād)

Activity 2

Handwriting practice. *Try to show your handwriting to an Arabic-speaking teacher or friend.*

Activity 3

2	أمين	7	زيدان
1	منير	9	ميدو
4	خيري	10	حبيب
3	حمدي	8	شحاتة
5	أبو زيد	11	نصري
		6	حسن

Activity 4

name	relationship to Sara	job
Sara	—	teacher
Hassan	husband	correspondant
Yasmin	daughter	accountant
Amin	son	engineer
Samira	mother	nurse

Activity 5

1 هم نجّارون.
2 هم خبّازون.
3 نحن مهندسون.
4 هنّ مدرّسات.
5 نحن محاسبات.
6 هم مدرّسون.
7 هنّ مهندسات.
8 هنّ ممرّضات.

Activity 6

أنت: ما عملك يا سارة؟ mā ɛamalik yā sāra?

سارة: أنا مدرّسة. وأنت؟ anā mudarrisa. w-anta(-i)?

أنت: أنا طالب(ة). أبي خبّاز. anā ṭālib(a). abī khabbāz.

سارة: آه! أنا أخي خبّاز! āh! anā akhī khabbāz!

أنت: ما عمل زوجك؟ mā ɛamal zawjik?

سارة: هو مراسل. huwa murāsil.

أنت: وابنك وبنتك؟ wa-ibnik wa-bintik?

سارة: أمين مهندس وياسمين محاسبة.
amīn muhandis wa-yāsmīn muḥāsiba.

أنت: ما شاء الله! mā shā' allāh!

unit 5 Describing things

Activity 1

1c, 2a, 3e, 4d, 5f, 6b

Activity 2

Handwriting practice. *Try to show your handwriting to an Arabic-speaking teacher or friend.*

Activity 3

1 قَلَم 2 دَرّاجة 3 كِتاب 4 خَيمة
5 قَميص 6 سَيّارة 7 خاتِم 8 مِفتاح
9 كَلب 10 حَقيبة

Activity 4

هذه...	هذا...
هذه درّاجة.	هذا قلم.
هذه خيمة.	هذا كتاب.
هذه سيّارة.	هذا قميص.
هذه حقيبة.	هذا خاتم.
	هذا مفتاح.
	هذا كلب.

Activity 5

1 ✔ 2 ✗ 3 ✔ 4 ✔ 5 ✗ 6 ✔ 7 ✗ 8 ✔

Activity 6

1 البيت 2 الولد 3 النهر 4 الزجاجة
5 المفتاح 6 الجريدة 7 التلميذ 8 القلم
9 المدينة 10 الخبّاز

Activity 7

أنت: صباح الخير. ṣabāḥ al-khayr

البائع: صباح النور. ṣabāḥ an-nūr

أنت: ممكن قلم من فضلك؟ mumkin qalam min faḍlak.

البائع: هذا القلم؟ hādhā l-qalam?

أنت: لا، أريد الأسود. lā, urīd al-aswad.

البائع: تَفَضَّل(ي). tafaḍḍal(ī).

أنت: هذا القلم مكسور! hādhā l-qalam maksūr!

البائع: تفضّل(ي). هذا القلم سليم.
tafaḍḍal(ī). hādhā l-qalam salīm.

أنت: شكراً shukran.

البائع: مع السلامة. maɛa s-salāma.

أنت: مع السلامة. maɛa s-salāma.

unit 6 Where is it?

Activity 1

at the end	in the middle	at the beginning	letter
ـط	ـطـ	طـ	ط (ṭā')
ـظ	ـظـ	ظـ	ظ (ẓā')
ـع	ـعـ	عـ	ع (ɛayn)
ـغ	ـغـ	غـ	غ (ghayn)

Activity 2

1 عرب 2 طالب 3 عمل 4 غزّة

5 مالطة 6 بغداد 7 قطر 8 أبوظبي

Activity 3

1e, 2f, 3a, 4c, 5b, 6d

Activity 4

Handwriting practice. *Try to show your handwriting to an Arabic-speaking teacher or friend.*

Activity 5

1 الخاتم تحت الكرسيّ. 2 المفتاح في الباب.

3 الشبّاك فوق السرير. 4 هل الكتاب فيالسيّارة؟

5 هل الحقيبة على الخزانة؟ 6 الصورة بجانب التليفزيون.

7 السرير بين السيّارة والخيمة.

8 هل الدراجة بين الشبّاك والمائدة؟

Activity 6

Free writing. *Try to show your sentences to an Arabic-speaking teacher or friend.*

Activity 7

1 هل هذا سرير؟ 2 هل هذا شبّاك؟

3 هل هذه صورة؟ 4 هل هذا باب؟

5 هل هذا تليفزيون؟ 6 هل هذه خزانة؟

7 هل هذا كرسيّ؟ 8 هل هذه مائدة؟

Activity 8

أنت: مساء الخير. masā' al-khayr

المتر: مساء النور. masā' an-nūr.

أنت: أريد مائدة. urīd mā'ida.

المتر: نعم. naعam.

أنت: مائدة بجانب الشبّاك من فضلك.
mā'ida bi-jānib ash-shabbāk, min faḍlak.

المتر: هذه المائدة؟ hādhihi l-mā'ida?

أنت: نعم. المائدة تحت الصورة.
naعam. al-mā'ida taḥt aṣ-ṣūra.

المتر: تَفَضَّل(ي). tafaḍḍal(ī).

أنت: جميل! شكراً jamīl. shukran!

unit 7 Describing places

Activity 1

Handwriting practice. *Try to show your handwriting to an Arabic-speaking teacher or friend.*

Activity 2

1 مصنع صغير 2 المصنع الصغير

3 مدينة كبيرة 4 المدينة الكبيرة

5 قميصي الجديد 6 كلبه الأسود

7 هو قويّ 8 هي بنت طويلة

Activity 3

1 Beirut (بيروت); **2** yes; **3** large; **4** yes; **5** no; **6** in the centre of town; **7** an old, beautiful house; **8** an ugly factory and a large hospital; **9** because the old house is dwarfed on both sides by the large buildings; **10** 'Your son, Yusuf'

Activity 4

✗ 1 ✗2 ✔3 ✔4 ✗5 ✗6 ✗7 ✔8

✔9 ✔10 ✗11 ✗12 ✔13 ✔14 ✔15 ✗16

✔17 ✗18

Activity 5

في هذه الصورة هناك شجرة كبيرة. أمام الشجرة هناك مائدة ثقيلة وكرسيّ. بجانب الكرسيّ هناك دجاجة صغيرة.

في وسط الصورة هناك ولد وهو على المائدة.

بجانب الولد هناك بنت. كلب البنت أسود وأبيض.

على المائدة هناك زجاجة كولا ووردة ولكن ليس هناك قلم أو كتاب.

Activity 6

أنت: صباح الخير. ṣabāḥ al-khayr

الرجل: صباح النور. ṣabāḥ an-nūr

أنت: هل هناك بنك في المدينة؟ hal hunāka bank fīl-madīna?

الرجل: نعم. بجانب المدرسة. naعam. bijānib al-madrasa.

أنت: على يمين المدرسة؟ عalā yamīn al-madrasa?

الرجل: لا، على يسارها. lā, عalā yasār-hā.

أنت: شكراً. مع السلامة. shukran. maعa s-salāma.

الرجل: مع السلامة. maعa s-salāma.

unit 8 Review

Activity 1

sun/moon letter	Arabic script	name of letter	sun/moon letter	Arabic script	name of letter
sun	ض	ḍād	moon	ا	alif
sun	ط	ṭā'	moon	ب	bā'
sun	ظ	ẓā'	sun	ت	tā'
moon	ع	ع ayn	sun	ث	thā'
moon	غ	ghayn	moon	ج	jīm
moon	ف	fā'	moon	ح	ḥā'
moon	ق	qāf	moon	خ	khā'
moon	ك	kāf	sun	د	dāl
sun	ل	lām	sun	ذ	dhāl
moon	م	mīm	sun	ر	rā'
sun	ن	nūn	sun	ز	zāy
moon	ه	hā'	sun	س	sīn
moon	و	wāw	sun	ش	shīn
moon	ي	yā'	sun	ص	ṣād

Activity 2

ص 3				خ 2		ب 1					
و		خ 7		ب	س	ا	ح	م 6		ا 5	ل 4
ر		ز		ا		ب		ك	ن	ب 8	
ة	ج	ا	ج	ز 9				س			
		ن				ت 11	ر	و	ش 10		
		ة	ب	ي 14	ق	ح 13		ر	ا	م	ح 12
				س		ت			ر		
م 17		ب 16		ا				م	ع	ن 15	
ص		ي	س	ر	ك 19		خ 18			ه	
ن	ي	ت 21			ل		ا		د	ر	و 20
ع					ب	ا	ت	ك 22			
							م				

Activity 3

1 بيتها 2 أبي 3 كتابه 4 غرفتي
5 ابنكَ 6 درّاجتكِ 7 زوجها 8 مدرستنا
9 مدينتهم 10 سيّارتهم

Activity 4

1F (student), 2F (engineer), 3T, 4T, 5F, 6T, 7F, 8T, 9T, 10F

Activity 5

1 الجريدة تحت الكرسيّ. 2 هناك كلب في الغرفة.
3 ليس هناك مدرسة في هذه المدينة. 4 هل بيتكَ كبير؟
5 هذه هي حقيبة زين. 6 أين أمّي؟ هي في البنك.

Activity 6

From Unit 8, the answers to the end-of-unit conversations include only your missing lines.

أنت: اسمي توم لويس. ismī Tom Lewis.

أنت: شكراً. أين غرفتنا؟ shukran. ayna ghurfat(u)nā?

أنت: الحقيبة في السيّارة. هي ثقيلة.
al-ḥaqība fīs-sayyāra. hiya thaqīla.

أنت: وهل هناك إنترنت في الغرفة؟
wa-hal hunāka internet fīl-ghurfa?

أنت: شكراً. shukran.

unit 9 Countries and people

Activity 1

1d, 2e, 3i, 4j, 5h, 6a, 7f, 8c, 9g, 10b

Activity 2

1 عمّان في شمال الأردن. 2 طرابلس في غرب ليبيا.
3 نيو يورك في شرق أمريكا. 4 لندن في جنوب إنجلترا.
5 بيروت في غرب لبنان. 6 *your [nearest] city*

Activity 3

Name	Nationality	Home town
Tom	English	Oxford
Natalia	Russian	Moscow
Maria	American	Los Angeles
Amna	Libyan	Tripoli
Ahmed	Saudi	Jeddah

Activity 4

1 هو فرنسيّ. 2 هو عراقيّ. 3 هي سوريّة.
4 هو إنجليزيّ. 5 هي سودانيّة. 6 هم مصريّون.
7 هم إيطاليون. 8 هنّ يابانيّات.

Activity 5

جاك فرنسيّ من باريس. أبو جاك من تولوز في جنوب فرنسا ولكن أمّه من بيروت في لبنان. جاك محاسب في البنك اللبنانيّ في وسط المدينة. أبو جاك مهندس في مصنع صغير وأُخته مراسلة لِجريدة لُبنانيّة في باريس. أمّ جاك ممرّضة في مستشفى بجانب بَيتهم.

Activity 6

Free writing. *Try to show your description to an Arabic-speaking teacher or friend.*

Activity 7

أنت: أنت من أين يا سارة؟ anti min ayna yā sāra?

أنت: أنا إنجليزي(ة)... anā ingilīzīyya...

ولكن أمّي أمريكيّة. wa-lākinn ummī amrīkīyya.

أنت: أنا من ليدز. anā min Leeds.

أنت: هي في شمال إنجلترا. hiya fī shamāl ingiltarā.

أنت: لا، هي مدينة كبيرة. la, hiya madīna kabīra.

unit 10 Counting things

Activity 1

٦a, ٣b, ١c, ٧d, ٤e, ١٠f, ٢g, ٩h, ٨i, ٥j

Order: c, g, b, e, j, a, d, i, h, f

Activity 2

١ أربعة جنيهات ٢ ستّة جنيهات ٣ ثلاثة جنيهات

٤ عشرة جنيهات ٥ سبعة جنيهات ٦ جنيه واحد

٧ ثمانية جنيهات ٨ تسعة جنيهات

Activity 3

١ موز ٢ تفّاح ٣ صندل ٤ طبق ٥ تي-شيرت

٦ طماطم ٧ طبلة ٨ منجة ٩ سلّة ١٠ قلادة

Activity 4

١ سوقان/ين ٢ طبقان/ين ٣ سلّتان/ين ٤ كيسان/ين

٥ قميصان/ين ٦ خاتمان/ين ٧ طبلتان/ين

٨ حقيبتان/ين ٩ قلمان/ين ١٠ قلادتان/ين

Activity 5

– أهلاً. صباح الخير!

– صباح النور. هل عِندَكُم صَندَل؟

– نعم. عِندَنا هذا الصندل.

– لا، أريد صندل جِلد من فضلك.

– صندل جلد؟ الصندل الأبيَض جميل.

– جميل. بكم هذا، من فضلك؟

– بعشرة جنيهات.

– تفضّل. عشرة جنيهات.

– شكراً. مع السلامة.

Activity 6

١ بكم الطبلة؟ ٢ بكم كيلو التفّاح؟

٣ القلادة بعشرة جنيهات. ٤ السلّة بسبعة جنيهات.

٥ كيلو الطماطم بثلاثة جنيهات. ٦ بكم طبق النُحاس؟

٧ صندل الجلد بثمانية جنيهات.

Activity 7

أنت: هل عندكم برتقال؟ hal ʿindakum burtuqāl?

أنت: كيلو المصريّ من فضلك. kīlū al-miṣrīy min faḍlak.

أنت: وبكم البطاطس؟ wa-bikam al-baṭāṭis?

أنت: ثلاثة كيلو من فضلك. بكم هذا؟ thalātha kīlū min faḍlak. bikam hādhā?

أنت: تفضّل. هل عندك كيس؟ tafaḍḍal. hal ʿindak kīs?

unit 11 Plurals and colours

Activity 1

plural	meaning	root letters	word
أقلام	pen	ق/ل/م	قلَم
أطباق	plate	ط/ب/ق	طَبق
قلوب	heart	ق/ل/ب	قَلب
مدرّسون	teacher	د/ر/س	مُدَرِّس
أصحاب	friend	ص/ح/ب	صاحِب
سيّارات	car	س/ي/ر	سيّارة
سيوف	sword	س/ي/ف	سَيف
أولاد	boy	و/ل/د	وَلَد
ألوان	colour	ل/و/ن	لَون
حفلات	party	ح/ف/ل	حَفلة
أكواب	cup/glass	ك/و/ب	كوب
شموع	candle	ش/م/ع	شَمعة
مراسلون	correspondent	ر/س/ل	مُراسِل
أكياس	bag	ك/ي/س	كيس
ممرّضات	nurse	م/ر/ض	مُمَرِّضة

Activity 2

١ هذه هي أقلامي. ٢ هذه هي أكوابي ٣ هذا هو كوبي.

٤ هذه هي أطباقي. ٥ هذه هي سيّارتي. ٦ هذه هي سيوفي.

٧ هؤلاء هم أولادي. ٨ هذه هي حقيبتي.

٩ هذا هو مفتاحي. ١٠ هذه هي شموعي.

Activity 3

You should have revealed a yellow house with a garden, two windows, a black door and a red roof.

Activity 4

who?	item(s)	description
Dad	shirt	white (cotton) for parties
Tariq	bag	black leather for school
Randa	pens	for writing (red and black)
Adil	tent	blue (lightweight)
Mum	films	old French
Nunu	sandals	small plastic (green)
Mimi	hat	yellow (cotton or silk)

Activity 5

أنت: أريد تي–شيرت قطن. urīd tī-shīrt quṭn.

أنت: أفضّل الأزرق. ufaḍḍal al-azraq.

أنت: وهل عندكم قبّعات قطن؟
wa-hal ؏indakum qubba؏āt quṭn?

أنت: القبعة البيضاء. al-qubba؏a al-bayḍā'.

أنت: تفضّل. شكراً. tafaḍḍal. shukran.

unit 12 What happened yesterday

Activity 1

١d, ٢h, ٣j, ٤a, ٥g, ٦i, ٧b, ٨c, ٩f, ١٠e

Activity 2

١ شربتُ فنجان شاي.
٢ أكلتُ دجاجة/دجاجاً.
٣ جلستُ على كرسيّ.
٤ كتبتُ خطاباً/خطابات.
٥ ذهبتُ إلى البنك.
٦ رجعتُ إلى البيت.
٧ وجدتُ مفتاحي/المفتاح.
٨ فتحتُ الباب.

Activity 3

١ ذَهَبَتْ ٢ شَرِبْتُ ٣ كَتَبَ ٤ فَتَحْتَ ٥ أَكَلْتِ
٦ وَجَدْتَ ٧ خَرَجَ ٨ جَلَسْتِ ٩ سَمِعَتْ ١٠ فَعَلْتُ

Activity 4

NAME	OCCUPATION	YESTERDAY			
		did what in day?	did what pm?	ate what?	drank what?
Waheed	correspondent	went to office wrote about theft	sat with wife	fish	coffee
Mary	nurse	went to hospital went to market	wrote a letter to sister	falafel	tea
Warda	pupil	went to school went to friend's house	watched TV	cola	pizza

Activity 5

1 in the south of Lebanon; 2 by bus; 3 the old city; 4 three; 5 gold, bakers' and fishmongers' markets; 6 old yellow houses; 7 a Lebanese restaurant; 8 falafel and labna (yoghurt dip); 9 in the evening; 10 'What did you do yesterday?'

Activity 6

خَرَجَ يوسف أمس صباحاً وذَهَبَ بالباص إلى صَيداء، وهي مدينة جميلة في جنوب لبنان.

أولاً ذهب إلى المدينة القديمة وَوَجَدَ أسواق الذهب والخبّازين والسَمّاكين وبيوتاً قديمة صَفراء. بعد ذلك ذهب إلى مطعم لبنانيّ و أكل فَلافِل ولَبنة. شرب قهوة عربيّة. أخيراً رجع إلى بيروت مساءً.

Activity 7

أنت: ذهبتُ إلى سوق الذهب. dhahabtu ilā sūq adh-dhahab.

أنت: وجدتُ قلادة لأختي. wajadtu qilāda li-ukhtī.

أنت: أكلتُ في مطعم لبنانيّ. alkaltu fī maṭ؏am lubnānīy.

أنت: شربتُ قهوة عربيّة. sharibtu qahwa ؏arabīyya.

أنت: لا. كتبتُ إيميل لأصحابي. lā. katabtu īmayl li-aṣḥābī.

unit 13 Wish you were here

Activity 1

plural	meaning	root letters	word
كِلاب	dog	ك/ل/ب	كَلب
رِجال	man	ر/ج/ل	رَجُل
صُوَر	picture	ص/و/ر	صورة
جِبال	mountain	ج/ب/ل	جَبَل
لُعَب	game	ل/ع/ب	لُعبة
غُرَف	room	غ/ر/ف	غُرفة
بِحار	sea	ب/ح/ر	بَحر
جِمال	camel	ج/م/ل	جَمَل
عُلَب	box	ع/ل/ب	عُلبة

Activity 2

f, m, b, h, k, c, i, g, n, a, l, j, d, e

Activity 3

وجدنا سبعة جِمال.
وجدنا ثلاث سيّارات.
وجدنا أربع درّاجات.
وجدنا ثلاث وثلاثين عُلبة.
وجدنا عشر صُوَر.
وجدنا خمسة عشر شَيخاً.
وجدنا ستّة كِلاب.
وجدنا خمسين طَبلة.
وجدنا عشرين طَبَقاً.
وجدنا ست وثمانين لُعبة.
وجدنا أربعة عشر حِماراً.
وجدنا تسعة أولاد.

Activity 4

١ تونس ٢ حارّ ٣ ٤٠ ٤ البحر
٥ القلعة ٦ سمكاً ٧ السوق ٨ الفندق

Activity 5

١ عزيزتي صفاء ٢ حارّ جدّاً ٣ في الشمال الشرقي
٤ شجر وجبال ٥ أنا والأولاد ٦ القلعة القديمة
٧ سمك بالكُسكُس ٨ مع تَحياتي

Activity 6

أنت: نحن في مدينة أفينيون. naḥnu fī madīnat afīnyūn.

أنت: الطقس بارد. درجة الحرارة ١٥.
aṭ-ṭaqṣ bārid. darajat al-ḥarāra khamsat ؏ashar.

أنت: لا، وجدنا بيتاً في المدينة القديمة.
la, wajadnā bayt(an) fīl-madīna al-qadīma.

أنت: أمس ذهبنا إلى القصر القديم... وجلسنا بجانب النهر..
ams dhahabnā ilā l-qaṣr al-qadīm... wa-jalasnā bijānib an-nahr.

أنت: ماذا فعلت أمس يا تامر؟ mādhā fa؏alta ams yā tāmir?

unit 14 All the president's men

Activity 1

١ يوم السبت ٢ يوم الأحد ٣ يوم الاثنين ٤ يوم الثلاثاء
٥ يوم الأربعاء ٦ يوم الخميس ٧ يوم الجمعة

Activity 2

يوم الأسبوع	الصورة	ماذا فعل طارق؟
الثلاثاء	٢	حضر معرض صُوَر.
الأربعاء	٥	أكل في مطعم إيرانيّ.
الخميس	٧	ذهب إلى البنك صباحاً.
السبت	٦	كتب إيميل لإبن أخته.
الجمعة	٣	شرب قهوة في بيت صاحبه.
الأحد	٤	لعب مع الكلب.
الاثنين	١	جلس مع أمّه.

Activity 3

plural فعلاء	person فعيل	noun فعالة	root letters
سُفَراء ambassadors	سَفير ambassador	سِفارة embassy	س/ف/ر
وُزَراء ministers	وَزير minister	وِزارة ministry	و/ز/ر
وُكَلاء agents	وَكيل agent	وِكالة agency	و/ك/ل
زُعَماء leaders	زَعيم leader	زِعامة leadership	ز/ع/م
رُؤَساء presidents	رَئيس president	رِئاسة presidency	ر/ء/س
أُمَراء princes/emirs	أمير prince/emir	إمارة emirate	ء/م/ر

Activity 4

ا ج ت م ا ع
و ك ا ل ة
س ف ا ر ة
و ز ا ر ة
م ع ر ض
م ؤ ت م ر
م ج ل س

Additional vocabulary: جَلَسة عَمَل *(working session)*

Activity 5

١e, ٢g, ٣i, ٤f, ٥d, ٦j, ٧a, ٨h, ٩b, ١٠c

Activity 6

١ تعليميّ ٢ زراعيّ ٣ دفاعيّ ٤ اقتصاديّ
٥ صناعيّ ٦ حكوميّ ٧ ثقافيّ ٨ صحّيّ

Activity 7

١d, ٢g, ٣a, ٤i, ٥h, ٦j, ٧b, ٨f, ٩e, ١٠c

Activity 8

أنت: ذهبتُ إلى وزارة الصناعة.
dhahabtu ilā wizārat al-ṣināع a.

أنت: حضرتُ مؤتمراً كبيراً. ḥaḍartu mu'tamar(an) kabīr(an).

أنت: مع مهندسين من الشرق الأوسط.
maع a muhandisīn min ash-sharq al-awsaṭ.

أنت: رئيس الوزراء حضر الافتتاح.
ra'īs al-wuzarā ḥaḍara l-iftitāḥ.

أنت: نعم وأنا جلستُ بجانبه!
naع am, wa-āna jalastu bijānibuh!

unit 15 Review

Activity 1

في الشبّاك هناك خمسة جمال، خمسة عشر كلباً، ثلاثة عشر كتاباً، سبعة أقلام، ستّة قُلوب، ثلاث درّاجات، ستّة عشر سَيفاً، ثلاثة تليفونات، أربع سيّارات، أربعة عشر شمعة.

Activity 2

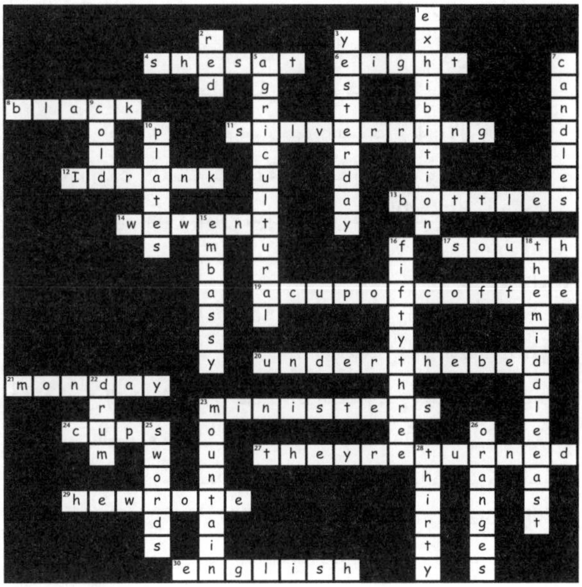

Activity 3

١f, ٢g, ٣h, ٤e, ٥c, ٦d, ٧b, ٨a

Activity 4

Free writing. *Try to show your postcard to an Arabic-speaking teacher or friend.*

Activity 5

١ وجدتُ المفتاح تحت الكرسيّ. ٢ الطقس حارّ جدّاً في عُمان.
٣ حضرنا حفلة في السفارة. ٤ هل ذهبتُم إلى المتحف؟
٥ وصلوا (يوم) الأحد. ٦ جلست على الكرسيّ الأسود بجانب الباب.

Activity 6

أنت: هل وجدتِ حقيبتك؟ hal wajadti ḥaqībatik?

أنت: أين ذهبتِ أمس؟ ayna dhahabti ams?

أنت: أين جلستِ في المطعم؟ ayna jalasti fil-maṭɛam?

أنت: وكيف رجعتِ إلى البيت؟ wa-kayfa rajaɛti ilā l-bayt?

أنت: آه... هل حقيبتك سوداء؟ āh... hal ḥaqībatik sawdā'?

أنت: نعم، بين المقعد والباب! naɛam, bayna l-miqɛad wal-bāb!

Unit 16 Every day

Activity 1

١ الساعة الثالثة	٢ الساعة الخامسة
٣ الساعة السابعة	٤ الساعة الرابعة
٥ الساعة السادسة والنصف	٦ الساعة العاشرة والنصف
٧ الساعة التاسعة والربع	٨ الساعة الواحدة والربع
٩ الساعة الخامسة إلا ربعاً	١٠ الساعة الثامنة إلا ربعاً

Activity 2

سامي مهندس ميكانيكيّ. كلّ يوم يَغسِل وَجهَهُ الساعة السادسة ويَلبِس مَلابِس العمل. ثُمّ يَأكُل الإفطار الساعة السادسة والنصف. يَخرُج من البيت الساعة السابعة ويَذهَب إلى مَصنَع السيّارات بالقطار. يَرجَع من المصنع إلى البيت الساعة الرابعة والرُّبع ويَرسِم صُوراً للشَّجَر والجِبال والأنهار بالألوان. يأكل العَشاء الساعة الثامنة إلا ربعاً وبعد ذلك يَشرَب فنجان شاي. أخيراً يَلبِس البيجاما ويَنام الساعة العاشرة.

Activity 3

١e, ٢a, ٣i, ٤k, ٥j, ٦m, ٧l, ٨f, ٩d, ١٠h, ١١g, ١٢c, ١٣b

Activity 4

١ يدرُسون الجغرافيا من الساعة التاسعة حتّى العاشرة إلا ربعاً.

٢ يدرُسون العربيّة من الساعة العاشرة إلا ربعاً حتّى الحادية عشرة.

٣ يدرُسون الكيمياء من الساعة الحادية عشرة حتّى الثانية عشرة والنصف.

٤ يأكلون الغداء من الساعة الثانية عشرة والنصف حتّى الثانية والربع.

٥ يدرُسون الرياضيّات من الساعة الثانية والربع حتّى الساعة الثالثة.

٦ يدرُسون الموسيقى من الساعة الثالثة حتّى الرابعة إلا ربعاً.

Activity 5

١ تَذهَب	٢ أَشرَب	٣ يدرُسون	٤ نَغسِل
٥ تَأكُلين	٦ تَحضُر	٧ تَلبَسون	٨ يكتُبون

يا أولاد، هل تلبسون البيجامات؟

كلّ يوم أنا وأخي نغسل الأطباق بعد العشاء.

بعد الغداء أجلس في كرسيّ وأشرب فنجان قهوة.

هم يدرسون التاريخ من الساعة التاسعة حتّى الساعة العاشرة.

لماذا لا تحضر المُحاضرات في الجامعة، يا أحمد؟

Activity 6

أنت: نأكل الإفطار الساعة الثامنة...
na'kul al-ifṭār as-sāɛa ath-thāmina...
وأخرج من البيت الثامنة والنصف.
w-akhruj min al-bayt ath-thāmina wan-niṣf.

أنت: أذهب إلى وسط المدينة بالقطار...
adh-hab ilā wasaṭ al-madīna bil-qiṭār...
ثمّ أذهب بالأتوبيس (بالباص) إلى المكتب.
thumma adh-hab bil-utūbīs (bil-bāṣ) ilā l-maktab.

أنت: أرجع الساعة الخامسة والنصف أو السادسة إلا ربعاً...
arjaɛ as-sāɛa al-khāmisa wan-niṣf aw as-sādisa ilā rubɛan...
ونأكل العشاء الساعة السابعة والنصف.
wa-na'kul al-ɛashā' as-sāɛa as-sābiɛa wan-niṣf.
وأنت؟ ماذا تفعل كلّ اليوم؟
wa-anta? mādhā tafɛal kull yawm?

Unit 17 Eating and drinking

Activity 1

ل	ا	ق	ت	ر	ب	ث	ف	ز	ك	س	ع
و	ن	ب	ي	ه	ة	م	ع	ط	م	ا	س
ك	خ	س	م	ص	ي	ا	ن	و	ك	ظ	ي
ا	ر	ك	س	ا	ش	ض	ل	ز	ر	أ	ر
ة	ظ	و	م	ل	ا	ك	ب	ج	و	ل	ح
ؤ	ل	ي	ط	ش	ي	ه	د	ة	ن	ب	ج
ن	ي	ت	ا	ي	ذ	ص	ر	غ	ة	ف	ع
ة	ز	ع	ط	س	ج	ك	ع	ك	س	ي	ب
ز	و	م	ذ	خ	ر	و	د	م	و	ث	ي
ي	ة	ض	ي	ب	ي	ل	ح	غ	ا	ن	ض
ت	ز	ب	ق	ز	ك	ا	ن	ي	ط	ب	ك
ل	ا	ق	ب	ه	ذ	ح	ة	ر	ي	ص	ع

Activity 2

١ كيس ٢ كيلو ٣ قطعة ٤ علبة ٥ علبة

٦ نصف لتر ٧ زجاجة ٨ لتر ٩ ربع كيلو ١٠ أنبوبة

Activity 3

بسكويت/زجاجة

برتقال/جبنة

كيس/تفّاح

أسنان/مسحوق

مسحوق/أسنان

مسحوق

Jamila didn't buy the toothpaste. The bill was 45 pounds.

Activity 4

verb form	root	meaning	present verb	past verb
Form II	ن/ظ/ف	to clean	يُنَظِّف	نَظَّف
Form II	س/خ/ن	to heat	يُسَخِّن	سَخَّن
Form I	ط/ب/خ	to cook	يَطبُخ	طَبَخ
Form II	ج/ه/ز	to prepare	يُجَهِّز	جَهَّز
Form IV	خ/ر/ج	to take out	يُخرِج	أَخرَج
Form II	ج/ر/ب	to try (out)	يُجَرِّب	جَرَّب
Form III	ع/و/ن	to help	يُعاوِن	عاوَن
Form II	ر/ت/ب	to tidy/arrange	يُرَتِّب	رَتَّب
Form I	ح/ج/ز	to book/reserve	يَحجِز	حَجَز

Activity 5

١ لم يُنَظِّف المطبخ. ٢ لم تُجَهِّز السلطة.
٣ لم يُخرِج الزبالة. ٤ لم تُسَخِّن الخبز.
٥ لم تَطبُخوا السمك. ٦ لم تَحجِز المطعم.
٧ لم تُعاوِنك راندا. ٨ لم يُرَتِّبوا غرفهم.

Activity 6

١ صلّحتُها ٢ سخّنتُه ٣ أخرجناها ٤ تُجَهِّزها
٥ يُنَظِّفه ٦ هل غسلتِها؟ ٧ هل أخذتَهُم؟

Activity 7

أنت: حجزتُ مائدة أمس. ḥajaztu mā'ida ams.
أنت: الاسم ريد. il-ism Reed.
أنت: يا جرسون! واحد دجاج بالأرزّ، من فضلك.
yā garsūn! waḥid dajāj bil-aruzz, min faḍlak.
أنت: وأريد سلطة الطماطم. wa-urīd salaṭa biṭ-ṭamāṭim.
أنت: آخذ عصير برتقال بارد. ākhudh ع aṣīr burtuqāl bārid.
أنت: نعم. آخذ رزّ بالحليب. naعam. ākhudh ruzz bil-ḥalīb.

unit 18 Comparing things

Activity 1

meaning	comparative	root letters	adjective
bigger/larger	أكبَر	ك/ب/ر	كبير
smaller	أصغَر	ص/غ/ر	صغير
more beautiful	أجمَل	ج/م/ل	جميل
cheaper	أرخَص	ر/خ/ص	رخيص
colder	أبرَد	ب/ر/د	بارد
shorter	أقصَر	ق/ص/ر	قصير
happier	أسعَد	س/ع/د	سَعيد
faster	أسرَع	س/ر/ع	سريع
heavier	أثقَل	ث/ق/ل	ثقيل
newer	أجَدّ	ج/د/د	جديد
lighter	أخَفّ	خ/ف/ف	خفيف
richer	أغنَى	غ/ن/ي	غَنِيّ
more important	أهَمّ	ه/م/م	هامّ
stronger	أقوَى	ق/و/ي	قَوِيّ
sweeter	أحلَى	ح/ل/و	حُلو

Activity 2

بيتي أكبر من بيتك. هو أكبر بيت في الشارع!
ابني أطول من ابنك. هو أطول ابن/ولد في الشارع!
بنتي أجمل من بنتك. هي أجمل بنت في الشارع!
خاتمي أقدم من خاتمك. هو أقدم خاتم في الشارع!
سيّارتي أسرع من سيّارتك. هي أسرع سيّارة في الشارع!
درّاجتي أجدّ من درّاجتك. هي أجدّ درّاجة في الشارع!
حقيبتي أخفّ من حقيبتك. هي أخفّ حقيبة في الشارع!
مشروبي أبرد من مشروبك. هو أبرد مشروب في الشارع!
عصيري أحلى من عصيرك. هو أحلى عصير في الشارع!
زوجي أغنى من زوجك. هو أغنى زوج/رجل في الشارع!
اجتماعي أهمّ من اجتماعك. هو أهم اجتماع في الشارع!
قلادتي أغلى من قلادتك. هي أغلى قلادة في الشارع!

Activity 3

1 baker, every day 4AM–7PM; **2** two; **3** Thursday, Friday and Saturday; **4** he was poor but now he is the richest man in town; **5** 90 bakeries in the Middle East; **6** in a large beautiful palace beside the river with his wife and children; **7** yes, he was happy: father = strong/taught him the love of work, mother = generous/beautiful/best cook in the street; **8** he eats warm bread and a piece of cheese for breakfast

Activity 4

١ مَخبَز/مَخابِز ٢ للوالدين ٣ ولذلك ٤ والده ٥ يَعيش
٦ كُنتُ سَعيداً ٧ حُبّ العَمَل ٨ خُبز دافِئ ٩ أشهَر ١٠ إلى اليوم

Activity 5

١ كُنتُ في البنك. ٦ كانَت الغرفة جميلة.
٢ كانوا في المصنع. ٧ كُنّا فقراء.
٣ كانَت طبّاخة. ٨ هل كُنتِ سعيدة؟
٤ هل كُنتَ الأطول؟ ٩ كانَت الأطباق جديدة.
٥ كان وزيراً. ١٠ هل كُنتُم أصحاباً؟

Activity 6

أنت: أتذكّر جدّي. atadhakkar jaddī.
أنت: منذ أربعين سنة كان ممثّلاً.
mundhu arbaعīn sana kāna mumaththil(an).
أنت: نعم. كان ممثّلاً شهيراً. naعam. kāna mumaththil(an) shahīr(an).
تعلّمتُ منه حبّ الأفلام. taعallamtu minuh ḥubb al-aflām.
أنت: كانت أفضل طبّاخة! kānat afḍal ṭabbākha!
كانت حلوياتها شهيّة. kānat ḥalawīyyāt(u)hā shahīyyā.
أنت: كنتُ أسعد طفل في الشارع! kuntu asعad ṭifl fīsh-shāriع!

unit 19 Future plans

Activity 1

١ يناير ٢ فبراير ٣ مارس ٤ أبريل
٥ مايو ٦ يونيو ٧ يوليو ٨ أغسطس
٩ سبتمبر ١٠ أكتوبر ١١ نوفمبر ١٢ ديسمبر

Activity 2

١ يوم الخميس، ١٥ يناير　　٢ يوم الجمعة ٢٠ مارس
٣ يوم الإثنين ٩ سبتمبر　　٤ يوم الثلاثاء ٢٢ يونيو
٥ يوم الأحد ١٤ فبراير　　٦ يوم الخميس ٣ أبريل
٧ يوم الأربعاء ١٢ يوليو　　٨ يوم السبت ٣١ أغسطس

Activity 3

Breakfast at 5:20AM; *Leave hotel at* 6AM; *Visits:* **1** Valley of the Kings, **2** Pharaonic museum, *(Lunch:* Amun Restaurant), **3** Karnak temple; *Return to hotel at* 8PM

Activity 4

١ سَتَزور أمّها في المستشفى الساعة التاسعة والنصف.
٢ سَتَحضُر اجتماعاً في المدرسة الساعة الحادية عشرة والثُلث.
٣ سَتَأكُل الغداء مع منيرة الساعة الواحدة (بعد الظُهر).
٤ سَتذهَب إلى البقّال الساعة الثانية والربع (بعد الظُهر).
٥ سَتكتُب إيميل للبنك الساعة الرابعة (بعد الظُهر).
٦ سَتغسِل الملابس الساعة الخامسة (بعد الظُهر).
٧ سَتَطبُخ اللحم للعشاء الساعة السادسة والنصف (مساءً).

Activity 5

١ سَيَحضُر　٢ سَأرجَع　٣ سَنَدرُس　٤ سَتُقلِع
٥ ستأكُل　٦ سَتَستَغرِق　٧ سَيُسافِر/سَيَزورون　٨ سَتُغادِرين

Activity 6

Free writing. *Try to show your description to an Arabic-speaking teacher or friend.*

Activity 7

أنت: غداً سنسافر إلى الأقصر بالقطار.
ghadan sa-nusāfir ilā l-aqṣur bil-qiṭār

أنت: نعم. ستستغرق ٩ ساعات. naعam. sa-tastaghriq tisعsāعāt.

أنت: سننام في القطار. sa-nanām fīl-qiṭār.

أنت: (يوم) السبت سنزور وادي الملوك.
(yawm) as-sabt sa-nazūr wādī al-mulūk.

وسنذهب إلى معبد الكرنك (يوم) الأحد.
wa sa-nadh-hab ilā maعbad al-karnak (yawm) al-aḥad.

unit 20 Review

Activity 1

verb form	root	meaning	present verb	past verb
Form V	ح/د/ث	to talk	يَتَحَدَّث	تَحَدَّث
Form III	غ/د/ر	to leave	يُغادِر	غادَر
Form IV	ق/ل/ع	to take off	يُقلِع	أقلَع
Form V	ذ/ك/ر	to remember	يَتَذَكَّر	تَذَكَّر
Form VIII	ج/م/ع	to meet	يجتَمِع	اِجتَمَع
Form X	غ/ر/ق	to last	يَستَغرِق	اِستَغرَق
Form VI	ع/و/ن	to cooperate	يَتَعاوَن	تَعاوَن
Form V	ع/ل/م	to learn	يَتَعَلَّم	تَعَلَّم
Form VII	ط/ل/ق	to move off	يَنطَلِق	اِنطَلَق

Activity 2

١ سَتَستَغرِق　٢ غادَرنا　٣ تَتَحَدّث　٤ تَتَذَكّر
٥ تَعاوَنوا　٦ أقلَعَت

Activity 3

Activity 4

١ ليس هناك...　٢ لا أشرب...　٣ لم تَذهَب...　٤ ليس عندنا...
٥ ليس هناك...　٦ لا نسمع...　٧ لم نُجَرِّب...　٨ لم تُغادروا...

Activity 5

٤ أكياس أرزّ　　أنبوبة معجون طماطم
زجاجة زيت　　٥ عُلَب تين
ربع كيلو بنّ　　ليمون أصفر

Activity 6

١ رجعتُ من دمشق يوم الجمعة.　٤ النيل هو أطول نهر في العالم.
٢ نتعلّم العربيّة في الجامعة.　٥ سأكتب لك خطاباً.
٣ أكلنا لحماً بالخبز العربيّ.　٦ سأتحدّث مع آدم غداً.

Activity 7

أنت: رجعنا من الأقصر الإثنين. rajaعnā min al-aqṣur al-ithnayn.

وأمس زرنا الأزهر. wa-ams zurna al-azhar.

هو أقدم جامعة في العالم. huwa aqdam jāmiعa fīl عālam.

أنت: ثمّ أكلنا حمام بالخبز العربيّ. كان شهيّاً!
thumma akalnā ḥamām bil-khubz al-عarabī. kāna shahīyyan!

أنت: ستقلع طائرتنا غداً الساعة الثالثة صباحاً.
sa-tuqliع ṭā'irat(u)nā ghadan as-sāعa ath-thālitha ṣabāḥan.

أنت: فسأقول "مع السلامة" الأن. fa sa-aqūl "maعa s-salāma" al-ān.

ولكني سأدرس العربيّة على الإنترنت...
wa-lākinnī sa-adrus al-عarabīyya عalā l-internet...

وسأكتب لك إيميل! wa sa-aktub lak(a) īmayl!